Rivers in Harness

By ALLAN H. CULLEN

Rivers in Harness

~~~~~~

The Story of Dams

CHILTON BOOKS

A Division of Chilton Company

Publishers

PHILADELPHIA AND NEW YORK

Contents

Rivers in Harness

1

The Flat-Tailed Engineers

~~~~~~

In the lakes and the streams of our nation, a very special corps of engineers has been busily at work for thousands of years. Sitting on their haunches, propped up by long, flat, scaly tails, these hard-working creatures double and triple in brass, not only doing the work of engineers but of contractors and construction men as well, as they go about their ordained task of building dams.

These creatures are, of course, beavers—nature's original dam-builders. These lowly bark-grubbing rodents have served as an inspiration for some of man's most awesome engineering achievements, the fantastic high dams, which, towering hundreds of feet, serve to control floods, provide vitally needed water for irrigation of crops, and yield electricity to power the swarming cities of humankind.

The beavers got there first. Long before the first shaky man-made dam was erected, eight or ten thousand years ago, the beavers were constructing their little engineering marvels. Some pessimists have been known to feel that the beaver folk will still be at their labors long after Hoover Dam and Grand Coulee Dam have crumbled to dust.

A look at the work of the beavers can give us a quick and clear understanding of the dam idea in its most basic form. A dam is a restraining barrier built across a stream or a river. It holds back the flow, causing a lake to form in the area just back of the dam. The waters of the artificial lake can then be used for recreation, or as a reservoir of drinking water, or they can be tapped off into surrounding farmland. The pent-up energy of the dammed river can be put to work turning a mill to grind wheat or corn, or turning a turbine to provide electrical power. And in times of flood the dam can serve as protection for the towns and cities farther down the river.

Beavers, of course, are not much interested in irrigation of farmland or in hydroelectric power, nor are they terribly concerned with flood control. The purpose of a beaver's dam is to create a place where the beaver family can live.

Beavers are members of the rodent family—relatives of the rats, mice, squirrels, and gophers. But beavers are aquatic by nature. Although they are mammals and must breathe air, they prefer to spend most of their time in the water, where they can move comfortably and agilely. On land they tend to be slow-moving and clumsy, an easy prey for their enemies.

To provide themselves with comfortable ponds to live in, beavers build dams across small streams. They do this by gnawing through trees and thus felling them. Beavers are magnificently equipped by nature to be lumberjacks as well as engineers. Their teeth are sharp as chisels, and never wear out or grow dull. The harder a beaver gnaws, the sharper his teeth become, because of their design.

A beaver can chew through a 4-inch tree in 20 minutes. The bark is used as food, and beavers prefer aspen, willow, poplar, and other tall, slim trees that grow in damp areas. Trees up to $2\frac{1}{2}$ feet in diameter often fall victim to the beaver's busy chisels. The beavers scurry miraculously out of harm's way as the trees fall.

Then the little engineers set to work. (Actually, beavers are not so little, by rodent standards. They grow to be 4 feet long, including more than a foot of tail, and weigh up to 50 or 60 pounds.) The beavers carefully trim the limbs and branches from the felled trees. Then they gnaw them into sections 4 or 5 feet long, and push them into the water at the site of the dam. Beaver engineers have devised a cunning transportation method that is used when all the trees along the banks of the stream have been cut down and they must move inland for their construction materials. They dig canals, about 2 feet wide, that lead from the stream to the clump of trees they are currently felling. Instead of hauling the felled trees overland for a hundred feet or more, they simply nudge them into the canal and *float* them to the stream!

At the dam site, beaver construction workers stack the logs one atop the other to block the flow of the stream. Mud and stones are scooped out of the stream bottom and used to plaster up the chinks in the dam. This serves the double purpose of strengthening the dam and of deepening the pond that the beaver is creating, a technique often copied by human dam-builders. When the stream bottom is not suitable for this function, the beavers pry clots of mud loose from the banks, hug them to their breasts, and paddle with hind legs to the dam sites. Plastering is done with the beaver's forepaws.

And so a quite elegant structure grows, built out of big logs buttressed with twigs, saplings, and branches, and sealed with mud and stones. The beavers build their dams as high as is necessary to create a backup of water big enough to serve as a beaver pond. The average beaver dam is 12 or 15 feet across the base and 5 or 6 feet high, but they often come much larger. In Estes Park, Colorado, a famous beaver dam was over a thousand feet long, while many in all parts of the country are 200 to 300 feet in length.

When the dam is completed, water backs up behind it, forming a pond, and in the pond the beavers build their "lodges," or homes. Although most of the beaver lodge is above water, the entrance is hidden below the surface. This keeps out nonswimming enemies like the wolverine, although it is little protection against the dangerous aquatic otter. The beavers repair damage to their dam immediately, so that the water level of the pond will never drop so low as to expose the hidden entrance of the lodge.

Another reason for keeping the pond deep is to prevent freezing in the winter. Although the surface of the beaver pond freezes over, there is always open water beneath the ice to provide a swimming area for the beavers, who store a supply of food for the winter alongside the dam and then swim to it under the ice at feeding time.

Beavers sometimes break up their dams deliberately to flood out an enemy. An old legend has it that the Okefenokee swamp of Florida and Georgia was created when beavers broke up their dams to flood Seminole Indians who were capturing baby beavers as pets. Beavers slap their tails against the water to make a warning sound.

Perhaps the idea of beavers breaking up their dams to hinder the advance of enemies seems a little farfetched. Yet this is another way in which men imitate beavers, for dams are frequently opened in time of war—as when the Dutch breached their dikes during World War II to bedevil the invading Germans, and when several years later the Russian Army, retreating from the Nazi marauders, partly destroyed the famous Dneprostroi Dam in the Ukraine to keep its power plant from falling into the hands of Hitler's men.

Beaver dams are useful to man as well as to their builders. A beaver pond accumulates silt brought down by its stream. When a beaver dam is breached, the silted water pours through, and the fertile silt is deposited over a wide area. This creates what farmers call a "beaver meadow," where crops grow particularly well.

The U.S. Government has put beavers to work—without pay—since 1938. In that year, a thousand beavers were introduced into Idaho to build small dams that would aid in soil and water conservation. Fast-flowing streams carve channels through fertile soil and carry it away; beaver dams halt the process. Today, many landowners use beavers to build dams for them in areas where man-made dams would be difficult or impossible to build. Beaver engineer corps can work in swampy, shifting ground where bulldozers fear to tread, and so beavers have created many a stock-water pond for a happy farmer.

This is a relatively recent development in American conservationist philosophy. From the 17th century through the 19th, beavers were hunted ruthlessly for their fur and all but exterminated in many parts of the continent. Today, beavers may not be trapped at all, except in areas where they have once again begun to flourish. And the recognition of their services in building dams that ease soil erosion problems has given them a value that far exceeds any they may have had as a source of fur.

Beaver dams are the simplest type of dam: the mere barrier. There are no gates or sluiceways in beaver dams, no turbines, no pumps or spillways or fish ladders or navigation locks, none of the myriad developments that we will be examining in detail in the chapters to come. A beaver dam is nothing more, nothing less, than a wall to hold back the water of a stream. It is a cleverly constructed wall, of course, an admirable and a fascinating creation—but just a wall across a stream, all in all.

2

Man-Made Dams

~~~~~~

THE first man-made dams probably were no more complex than beaver dams. It is altogether likely that the first human to think of building a dam got the idea from watching beavers at work. Beavers are found not only in North America but in parts of Europe and Asia, and in antiquity they were much more widely distributed than they are now. Men of keen intelligence in many parts of the world, thousands of years ago, would have had opportunities to watch the work of the beaver.

We have no way of knowing where or when the first man-made dam was built. We can, however, take an educated guess that it was constructed some 8,000 to 10,000 years ago, and that it was built either in the part of the Near East known as Mesopotamia, or in Egypt, or possibly in China.

We can guess at these three locations because it was there that the intelligence of man first ripened fully. Mesopotamia, Egypt, and China all had flourishing and highly sophisticated civilizations thousands of years before Europe or the Americas.

Considering the exciting climate of intellectual expansion in those three parts of the world during prehistoric times, it is almost a certainty that the dam idea must have originated in one of the three.

As for the date, well, we know that 5,000 years ago quite substantial dams were being built. Archeological evidence dates the ruins of these dams conclusively. Since in the relatively slow pace of development of prehistoric technology thousands of years must have been needed to refine the dam concept to the state it had reached in 3000 B.C., we can assume that the very first human dams are at least 3,000 to 5,000 years older.

Wherever and whenever it was built, that first dam was almost certainly an irrigation dam. Its designer may have observed beavers at work, or he may simply have leaped to the magical conclusion that seems so absurdly simple to us: that if you put a barrier across a stream, water will back up and a pond will be formed.

The first dam was probably a crude pile of mud and twigs and rocks, a good deal less cleverly constructed than a beaver dam. The builder must have had a difficult time of it, for even if he chose a placid stream to work in, the steady flow of the water must have tended to carry away his fill almost as fast as he could lay it down. But, working in a narrow channel at a time when the stream ran thinly, he finally was able to complete a barrier from one bank to the other.

Water began to rise.

A pond started to form.

The pond itself was useless except perhaps for swimming, but a second great invention gave it value: the irrigation canal. Our early engineer, digging laboriously with stones and sharpened sticks, hewed out crooked channels that led from his pond into the neighboring fields. Water began to flow off, quenching the thirst of the crops. No longer was the farmer completely at the mercies of the elements. He did not have to wait for rain to water his crops. In springtime, water could be collected in the reservoir behind the dam, and then it could be drawn off during the hot dusty days of summer to nourish the fields.

It seems so simple to us, so obvious. But nothing is obvious until it has been done for the first time. Look at the knowledge that had to be accumulated before the concepts of building dams and irrigation canals could emerge:

Men had to shift from gathering food to raising their own. They had to learn which crops to plant, and how to plant them. They had to make the fundamental discovery that without water crops will not grow. They had to learn how to dig and build. They had to come to understand the changing of the seasons, the time of flood and the time of drought.

It took thousands of years for these fundamental things to become part of mankind's growing and precious store of knowledge. And then the era of dam-building—of control over water—began.

The ancients built many dams whose ruins still exist. In Mesopotamia, between the Tigris and the Euphrates Rivers, a highly advanced culture emerged about 5,000 years ago. The earliest inhabitants of the area that we know much about were called the Sumerians, and they lived in the valley of the Euphrates. There they were troubled by damaging floods until they built a series of dikes to hold the rampaging waters back. The Sumerians had no stone, and so built their dikes out of heaped-up earth held in place by sun-dried brick. Mounded platforms kept the waters back. The southernmost part of their kingdom was originally a swamp; in the first land reclamation project known to man, embankments were constructed and drainage channels designed to turn the swamp land into fertile farmland. Over a period of several thousand years the Sumerians reclaimed thousands of acres from the swamp this way. Their cities rose out of the mud of the Persian Gulf, and so good a job of reclamation did they do that some of the Sumerian cities that were originally built on the shore of the Persian Gulf are now many miles inland, every square foot to the south of them having been reclaimed from the marsh.

After the Sumerians, the Babylonians came to rule in Mesopotamia, and this new race continued the great projects of
their predecessors. We know that the city of Babylon 4,000
years ago boasted an enormous canal, the Nahrwan, which
was 400 feet wide and 200 miles long. The Nahrwan carried
water for irrigation from the distant Tigris to the fields surrounding Babylon. A great dam across the river regulated the
water supply of the canal, building up the height of the flow
so that it would spill over into the ditch and begin the long
journey to Babylon.

Nothing today is left of these early Babylonian waterworks
but their memory. In northern Mesopotamia, though, a warlike
race akin to the Babylonians came to power some 3,000 years
ago, and they built lastingly, out of stone. These were the
Assyrians, who conquered the older civilizations of the East
in one of history's bloodiest pages.

The Assyrians built simple stone dams across the Tigris at
many points to divert water for irrigation. Mighty cities such
as Nineveh and Assur grew formidably powerful thanks to
the artificially induced fertility of their surrounding farmlands.
The Assyrians used not only canals but aqueducts—elevated
stone structures—to bring water to their cities. One of the finest
was built in the 8th century before Christ by the tyrannical
King Sennacherib, who ordered the construction of an aqueduct 50 miles long to bring water to Nineveh from a far-off
stream. The stream was dammed to direct the flow of water
into the aqueduct. (A dam built across a river for the primary
purpose of directing water into an aqueduct or canal is often
called a *weir*.)

Dam-building in Mesopotamia continued for a period of at
least 4,000 years. Soon after Sennacherib's time, however, Assyria fell to its enemies and its great cities were destroyed. The
dams gradually crumbled and the desert reclaimed its own.
Today, 2,500 years after the fall of Assyria, most of Mesopotamia (now Iraq) is desert land, having been shamefully neg-
lected since the time of Christ. Belatedly, the descendants of
the Assyrians and the Babylonians are once again starting to

harness the two great rivers, the Tigris and the Euphrates, and someday soon the valleys of Mesopotamia will once again be green and fertile. Until then, the shattered blocks of the Assyrian dams jut from the Tigris as reminders of the grandeur that once was.

THE DAMS OF EGYPT

Civilization flowered almost simultaneously in Mesopotamia and in nearby Egypt. While the Sumerians and their successors labored to reclaim land from the marshes and to channel the water of the Tigris and Euphrates into the farmlands, the country of the Pharaohs contended with the mighty Nile.

The Nile is Egypt's glory and her treasure, the source of her wealth and strength. But the Nile also has brought sorrow, flood, and devastation to Egypt. From the earliest days of civilization in Egypt, then, it was the concern of the country's rulers to create a system of canals to drain off the flood waters. This involved building weirs or barrages across the Nile at various points to induce the water into the canals, and thence to smaller canals and finally to irrigation ditches in the fields.

The huge river rises near Lake Tanganyika and flows northward more than 4,000 miles to the Mediterranean. Its drainage basin covers about 1,100,000 square miles, or approximately one tenth the area of the entire African continent.

Men settled in the valley of the Nile thousands of years ago, and by 3400 B.C. had achieved a high level of civilization, rivaling that of Sumer to the north and that of China far to the east. Originally the Nile Valley was a chain of reedy swamps and jungle regions, populated chiefly by snorting hippopotamuses. The prehistoric Egyptians set themselves the task of clearing away the swamps and making the land suitable for agriculture.

This they accomplished. During the thousands of years that this land-clearing phase lasted, the Egyptians grew to understand the annual flooding cycle of the Nile. During the spring and summer, the river would be low, and the land surrounding it felt the full brunt of the African sun. Then, late each summer, the rains began, to the south, in Ethiopia. The river gradually gathered strength, swelled, flooded as it raced northward. It would overleap its banks, carrying silt and decaying leaves and topsoil with it out of the south and spreading this fertile material over the land of the north.

Then the rains would cease, and the flooded river would recede, leaving behind the bounty it had brought—the fertile mud stripped from the fields of the south. The Egyptians could then plant their crops in this mud, by the end of October, yielding a harvest in the spring. Then the parching summer would come, followed by the rains and the floods, and the cycle would begin anew.

The Egyptians soon came to understand that each year their fields would be flooded in July, would soak until October, and then would be wondrously fertile through the mild winter. It became possible to predict the time of the flood and the time of the water's retreat almost to the day.

But, bountiful though the river's annual gift was, the Egyptians saw that it could be made even more useful if it were controlled. And so a staggeringly complex system of diversion dams came into being between the years 3400 B.C. and 1500 B.C. Dikes were built along the banks of the Nile, raising the river's channel to prevent indiscriminate flooding of the land. Then canals carried the water in an orderly way to the fields. During Egypt's golden millennia this dam system spread up and down the Nile to the great benefit of the country's agriculture.

There was plenty of labor available, though not always willingly. The same slaves who built the ponderous Pyramids could also haul stone for the dams, and the same engineers who devised those wonders of the ancient world could also turn their abilities to flood control projects.

All civilizations reach a point of decadence, and their works fall into ruin. This happened in Egypt in Roman times, when the Pharaohs had gone and the great era of Egyptian power was a thousand years and more in the past. The wonderful

waterworks of the Nile were allowed to fall into disrepair
and eventually yielded to the battering fury of the annual
floods. The best preserved of Egypt's ancient dams is not an
irrigation dam at all, but one that was used to create a reservoir of rain water for stoneworkers at an alabaster quarry.
It is in a ravine known as the Wadi Gerrawi, and it stretches
370 feet from one side of the ravine to the other. Originally
it was 270 feet thick, built of stone.

After a period of decay lasting more than ten centuries,
the Egyptians began to rebuild their canals and dams during
the era of the Moslems. A series of low dams was thrown up
across the Nile from the middle of the 18th century on, which
would run water into canals every 2 or 3 weeks, and then to the
fields. This permitted several crops to be grown in the Nile
Valley each year, rather than just the one winter crop in the
wake of the annual flood.

The first modern dam on the Nile was completed in 1902 at
Aswan. It was a major engineering project that would have
aroused keen excitement in the hearts of the wonderful engineers who designed the dams and monuments of ancient Egypt
thousands of years before. Since we have been discussing the
Nile, let us anticipate part of our story and leap out of the
time of the Pharaohs for a peek at this latter-day Aswan Dam.

Like its 3,000-year-old ancestors, this dam was designed
primarily to control the flooding of the Nile, to promote irrigation in the Nile Valley, and to further navigation along the
river. These were uses which the Pharaohs would have understood. As we will see in later chapters, dams had also come to
have other uses since the days of the pyramid-builders, and so
the Aswan Dam was also designed to serve as a producer of
electricity.

Aswan is 750 miles from the mouth of the Nile. The site
was chosen because the river at Aswan is shallow and has a
granite bed, on which a firm foundation could be erected. The
river flowed through five channels at Aswan, at an average
speed of 16 miles an hour.

The first step in damming any major river is to divert the

flow of water to permit construction. The engineers who worked at Aswan at the turn of the century accomplished this by building a circular barrage around the area chosen for the dam foundations on the east side. At low river, this enclosure was pumped out. The water was allowed to flow through the two channels on the west side while construction proceeded in the three eastern channels.

All the work had to be completed before the river flooded again. And so work teams labored round the clock, excavating to a depth of 40 feet in the riverbed to lay the foundations of the dam. In a single day, 3,600 tons of masonry were put in place—an epic feat for the time. With these foundations laid, sluice gates were installed and the river was turned back into the eastern channels while work continued to the two western ones. Finally, in 1902, at a cost of $15,000,000, the dam was completed. It stood 120 feet high from its foundations, ran 1½ miles from shore to shore, and was 100 feet thick at its base. Along the top it was 24 feet wide. A roadway ran along this upper rim.

The dam backed up a reservoir of 1 billion tons of water. One hundred and eighty sluices, 140 of them along the lower part of the dam and 40 of them along the upper, were built into the barrier. During flood time, the dam would build up its reservoir; then, during the hot months of drought, the accumulation of water could be released through the sluice gates and it would roll northward to moisten the dry fields of the upper valley.

The billion-ton reservoir was not enough. More water was needed for the thirsty fields of Egypt. In 1907, operations began to raise the crest of the dam by 23 feet, which would add 2,400,000,000 tons of water to the reservoir. To do this it was necessary to thicken the base of the dam, and it was done in a two-step process. First hundreds of steel rods were driven into the face of the old wall of the dam. The new masonry was built around these rods, with a space of 2 to 6 inches left open. Then, 2 years later, the space was filled with cement pumped in through flexible pipes. This was done to give the new masonry time to contract before it was joined to the old.

The dam was raised again after World War I, to give it a reservoir capacity of nearly 5 billion tons of water. But even this has been insufficient for Egypt's growing needs, and about a decade ago it was decided to build a *second* dam at Aswan —the Aswan High Dam.

Financing this projected giant proved to be a headache for Egypt. The cost of the 300-foot-high dam was due to approach a billion dollars, more than fifty times what the original Aswan Dam had cost. The government of Egypt approached both the United States and the Soviet Union for financial and technical assistance. In July 1956, Egyptian President Gamal Abdul Nasser announced that the United States, Great Britain, and the International Bank for Reconstruction and Development had agreed jointly to underwrite the Aswan High Dam project. (Today's dams are expensive projects even for the big powers to undertake!)

But immediately afterward, the offer of American aid was abruptly withdrawn by U.S. Secretary of State John Foster Dulles. Dulles gave, as his reasons for reneging, doubt as to the economic soundness of the dam scheme, and displeasure at Egypt's establishment of friendly relations with the Communist bloc. Thus the Aswan Dam seemed doomed to die for political reasons.

President Nasser retaliated angrily by seizing the Suez Canal and touching off a world crisis. Then, in 1958, the Soviet Union agreed to supply loans and technicians to build the dam. Work began officially on January 9, 1960, with a Russian grant of $400,000,000 easing the way.

The first aim of the dam-builders will be to dig a bypass canal a mile long, through which the waters of the Nile will run while construction is taking place in the riverbed. This canal must be blasted through solid granite cliffs 100 to 200 feet high, and a 7,500-man construction force is toiling day and night at this moment to complete the job. Once the river is diverted, construction of the dam itself can begin, with completion hopefully intended for 1967.

One sad aspect of dam-building is that villages and towns in the path of the reservoir must be flooded. This is particularly poignant in Egypt, where the Nile Valley is so rich with archeological treasure. When the original Aswan Dam was built in 1902, it caused the submersion of the island of Philae, on which is located the lovely temple of Isis. This temple, once eagerly visited by pilgrims from every part of the ancient world, now is nearly hidden by the waters of the reservoir, and emerges only for a short time every August, when it can be visited again. (The temple emerges because in August the sluice gates of the dam are opened to clean away the year's accumulation of silt. The pent-up water rushes through, carrying away the debris and muck, and leaving the temple above water until the gates are closed and the reservoir level has risen again.)

Philae, with its beautiful temple and its many other archeological points of interest, was not the only victim of the Aswan Dam's reservoir. Whole villages were swallowed up by the spreading waters, their inhabitants, of course, resettled by the Egyptian Government. Today it is possible to travel by boat up the Nile and look down at the rooftops of the drowned villages beneath the river's waters.

The archeological cost of the first Aswan Dam, however, is slight compared to the havoc the new dam will wreak. Its enormous reservoir, 367 miles long, will not only permanently submerge the temple of Isis on Philae, but will drown vast stretches of the valley above the dam, covering forever irreplaceable relics of the distant past. While workmen blast through the cliffs at Aswan, teams of archeologists work feverishly to recover as much as they can from the region to be drowned, knowing they have too little time to complete their work.

A major problem is Abu Simbel, a group of temples built by the Pharaoh Rameses II about 1200 B.C. At Abu Simbel, four immense statues, 65 feet high, have been cut out of the hillside to form the greatest rock-hewn monument of the ancient world, a powerful and unforgettable sight.

Abu Simbel is due to be flooded by the new reservoir. This would be an incalculable artistic loss, and so the Egyptian Government is planning to spend millions of dollars to save the monument by cutting it free of its hillside and *raising* it above the surface of the water. It is an extravagant scheme, but big dams seem to create extravagant problems. No one questions the need for the reservoir. But, though peasant villages can be replaced, Abu Simbel cannot. And so the cost of the dam grows greater—but a memorable part of Egypt's past will be preserved.

This discussion of the dams at Aswan has taken us far from antiquity. But it is important to grasp the continuity of the dam-building idea by seeing how the Nile has been dealt with over the ages.

In some of the lands of the Near East, antiquity is closer to the present than we may think. Sir William Willcocks, who planned the first Aswan Dam, discovered this when he ventured into Iraq to build the Hindiya Barrage across the Euphrates, near the site of ancient Babylon. This brick weir has recaptured a million acres from the desert.

Sir William used native Arab laborers, but he had difficulty getting them to use newfangled devices such as shovels and wheelbarrows. They preferred their age-old techniques for excavating and carrying away earth. An engineer explained at great length the advantages of European methods, only to be met with this reply:

"You people from the west! Why, a thousand years ago no one knew you. My people have been here since the days of Moses. Are *you* going to teach *us* how to carry earth?"

DAMS OF ANCIENT CHINA

Flood control has always been one of China's great problems. China's rivers change course with complete disregard for human activities, inundating areas that thought themselves safe from flood. A Chinese proverb has it that "Every eighty years the Yellow River is in flood, and every one hundred eighty years its course is changed."

The floods of China are devastating in their impact, almost beyond the comprehension of those who have had no first-hand experience with them. In 1931 the Yangtze rose 50 feet above its normal level, swept away miles of dikes, and flooded thousands of square miles of thickly populated countryside. Some 180,000 people perished—equivalent to the entire population of Nashville, Tennessee. And 25,000,000 were left homeless and close to starvation—as many people as dwell in New York City, Tokyo, and London combined.

To fight these floods, the Chinese early turned to a system of dikes lining the riverbanks. The earliest recorded flood control program was begun by the Emperor Yu in 2205 B.C., but doubtlessly Chinese rulers were building dikes long before history recorded their names. Emperor Yu had a twofold flood control system: the building of dikes and the deepening of river channels.

Deepening the channels, though, is no simple matter, the Chinese found out. And the rivers of China tend to be silty. The silt collects in the riverbeds, raising them. If the rivers are shallow, the dikes must be built high to contain them, and so for thousands of years the Chinese have built higher and higher dikes along the banks of the Yangtze, the Hwang Ho (Yellow River), and the other rivers of China. But frequent enemy attacks sapped dike-building energies, and from time to time the Chinese would destroy their own dikes to flood out the enemy, as they did in 1938 during the war with Japan.

Whereas dam-building in Egypt and Mesopotamia began for the purpose of irrigation and reservoir creation, flood control was the chief aim in ancient and modern China. There were, however, irrigation systems as well. The Tukiangyien system was built 2,300 years ago on the Min River, which comes down out of Tibet to cover a broad plain in China. A series of dams and dikes was erected where the river met the plain, and 500,000 acres were irrigated by this network of bamboo-and-rock structures to divert the water into canals.

OTHER DAMS OF ANTIQUITY

One of the greatest dams of the ancient world can be seen, in ruins, in a remote corner of the Arabian Desert. This is the Marib Dam in what is now the Kingdom of Yemen.

This imposing structure would certainly have been one of the Seven Wonders of the Ancient World, if only the Greeks who compiled that list had known of its existence! Here, a dozen centuries before Mohammed, a vanished race called the Sabeans built an impressive city, and erected a huge dam to supply it with water. Even today, it is not easy to visit Yemen or to see the Marib Dam, and we must rely on the accounts of those few archeologists who succeeded in penetrating to the desert wastes where it stands.

These include Wendell Phillips and Professor William F. Albright of Johns Hopkins University, who explored Yemen in 1950. In his book, *Qataban and Sheba,* Wendell Phillips describes the Marib Dam:

"Lying a few miles out from the old city, it is really a series of dams, sections of which are still standing. . . .

"We saw where whole sections of mountainside had been carved away alongside the dam to form spillways to irrigate the adjacent fields. The dam had served as the central control for the mass of waters pouring down from the mountains of Yemen, the spot from which it was distributed to create mile upon mile of green fields.

"Most amazing was the way the great stone walls had been put together. Huge boulders were so perfectly dressed that they fitted into each other like pieces in a jigsaw puzzle. We saw no trace of mortar of any kind, yet we looked at portions of the wall that were more than fifty feet high, standing as they had when Sheba's great artisans built them about 2,700 years ago.

"Other sections of the vast structure were missing, washed away no doubt by the great Sixth Century cloudburst."

The author is referring to an almost legendary flood that shattered the Marib Dam and put an end to the prosperity of the Sabeans. The Koran declares, "The people of Sheba had beautiful gardens with good fruit. Then the people turned away from God, and to punish them, He burst the dam, turning the good gardens into gardens bearing bitter fruit." And Wendell Phillips offers this fable as well:

"King Amr was informed by a soothsayer that if he saw a mouse digging into the dam, that would be a sign from God that the huge structure was about to give way. The King then went to the dam and saw a mouse which moved, with its tiny feet, a great stone that could not be budged by fifty men. And the next day the dam burst."

Of course, dams that have withstood the river torrent for ten centuries do not fall apart overnight, like the one-hoss shay. Rather, the process of deterioration goes on unnoticed for many years—until the final catastrophe, which comes as a shock and a surprise, though it should not. Archeologists feel that the Sabean civilization reached its peak of wealth by the beginning of the Christian era, and then went into a long, slow decline. During those latter years, the dam was permitted to fall into neglect. Leaks that would have been repaired immediately in the great days of Marib were allowed to go unchecked. The structure weakened gradually, until when the great cloudburst came the dam was unable to hold back the flood. It shattered; and the gardens of Marib reverted to the desert. But the shattering of the dam was the effect, and not the cause, of the Sabean decline.

Few have visited the Marib Dam. The first Westerners reached it in 1762, and several other expeditions observed it in the 19th century. The Phillips-Albright party was forced by the outbreak of a Yemeni civil war in 1951 to flee, leaving behind some of their equipment.

Another Arabian civilization that did extraordinary engineering work in the centuries before Christ left ruined dams in the Negev Desert of what is now Israel. These people were the Nabataeans, who flourished in that bleak desert amid green fields of plenty. Nelson Glueck, the famed archeologist and Biblical scholar, has called the Nabataeans "one of the most remarkable people that ever crossed the stage of history."

The Negev has an annual average of only 4 inches of rainfall. The rain comes only in the winter, and in sudden cloudbursts. The desert soil is hard and dry, and the rain does not sink in. Instead, it rushes down through dry gulches known as wadis, building up into fierce muddy torrents as the racing floods rip soil from the hills in their descent. The result is that for most of the year the desert is bone dry, but during the winter rains the wadis became channels for raging torrents.

The ancient Nabataeans reasoned that their only hope of developing agriculture was somehow to control the flow of water through the wadis, to harness these floods and utilize the water throughout the dry part of the year. They did this by building a series of stone terraces in the wadis to trap the water and slow its descent. The terraces began in the lesser wadis high on the hillsides, and continued downward. As the flood waters entered this series of steps, they would discharge their burden of fertile silt, so that after the floods crops could be grown in the terraces.

The main wadis were engineered more elaborately, divided by masonry walls into level plots. These filled with water during the floods, and as each overflowed, the water would spill into adjoining compartments on higher ground. Thus, instead of a single savage flow of water racing through the wadi and creating soil erosion, gentle ponds were formed, and water could be tapped off for irrigation and for storage in shaded reservoirs.

Some of the wadis had extremely deep channels, and here the terrace scheme was not workable. Here the Nabataeans built thick stone dams in series, to retard the flood flow and to lift the water to terraces along the banks of the wadi. There, stone conduits upstream of the dams diverted the flow into the fields. To prevent the watercourse from changing direction, massive stone walls were built along the entire length of the flood channel to maintain permanent boundaries.

This intricate and skilful flood-control system was a perfectly balanced job of engineering, since each component of the system functioned in harmony with every other. The floods were controlled, and water was stored against the dry months. From their own papyrus records we know that these desert folk raised barley, wheat, legumes, figs, grapes, and dates. We also know that their barley sowings gave over eight times the amount of seed sown, and the wheat sowings a sevenfold return. This compares favorably with farming today in the Negev, where, farther to the north where rainfall is heavier, and with the benefit of modern engineering, the best that can be accomplished is an elevenfold yield of barley and an eightfold yield of wheat.

In A.D. 106 the Nabataeans were occupied by a Roman army, and for the next six centuries they survived as subjects of Rome. After the rise of the Moslems, the Nabataean cities were gradually abandoned, and remained deserted until Israeli archeologists began to study them a decade ago in the hopes of learning their ancient secrets of flood control.

Elsewhere in the ancient world dams were built widely, chiefly for reservoir and irrigation purposes, sometimes for flood control as well. The ancient Romans built many great dams, some of which still survive in ruins throughout Europe and the Near East. In Ceylon, a reservoir is recorded as having been built as early as 504 B.C., while another, the Padavil-Colan Tank, was created through the erection of a barrier dike 11 miles long and 70 feet high, with a total volume of 17 million cubic yards of earth. A similar ancient dike in neighboring India was 30 miles long—and constructed without bulldozers!

Wherever there was an alternation of hot, dry weather and wet, rainy weather, dams and reservoirs became a necessity if agriculture was to be carried on all the year round. Thus the dam idea sprang up independently in many parts of the world. In the Western Hemisphere before the coming of the white man, for example, there was no commerce with the older nations of the world, no way to learn their secrets of dam-building. Yet irrigation canals and reservoirs were built by the Aztecs of Mexico and by other peoples of the New World. The Indians of our country's arid southwest built small irrigation dams 800 to 1,000 years ago. The idea has been a universal one.

THE MARBLE DAMS OF RAJPUTANA

Little known and inaccessible are two architectural wonders of India that deserve mention here, though they are not really dams of antiquity. These are the dams at Jai Samand and Raj Samand, in the Aravalli hills of India's State of Rajasthan (Rajputana). The most unusual feature of these two dams of the 17th century is that they are built of pure, polished white marble—so that they are probably the most beautiful dams ever built.

The smaller of the two dams is at Jai Samand (the Sea of Victory), an artificial lake more than 90 miles in circumference. Here the Rajput king Jai Singh commanded the construction of a dam 1,000 feet long to block the flow of a mountain stream. Flights of white marble steps extend the entire length of the dam to the water's edge, and along the top are marble palaces and open-arched pavilions of breathtaking beauty. Six half-sized marble elephants stand atop the Jai Samand dam, trunks raised as though to greet the rising sun each day with a trumpeting welcome.

The great artificial lake converts arid wastes into fertile rice and grazing fields. The wild gorge in which the dam stands is ringed with lofty hills. The lake itself, lying still on a moonlit night, reflects the palaces and the pavilions of Jai Singh's dam with perfection.

Twenty-five miles away is the second dam, Raj Samand. The lake here is not so great as at Jai Samand, but the engineering problems were far greater. The dam, built by a later king, Rana Raj Singh, cost $5,000,000—at a time when slave labor was plentiful. The dam is an irregular semicircle 3 *miles* long—all of it of white marble, tons upon tons of it, buttressed with thick ramparts of earth. Three terraces of steps drop to the water. Four elegantly carved Hindu arches ornament the lowest tier. Marble terraces reach out over the water as supports for three 12-pillared pavilions. Here the kings of Rajputana would sit in regal majesty, looking out over the shimmering lake.

Lovely as they are, these dams were built not merely for beauty's sake. In 1661 pestilence and famine had swept the kingdom of Rana Raj Singh. A chronicle of his day reports: "Instead of rain a pestilential vapor blew from the west. The streams dried up, fishes became extinct. Cities were depopulated, the seed of families lost. Trees were stripped of their bark and eaten. Foul things unknown as food were devoured. . . . Then the hope of all was lost, for *man ate man.*"

The two great dams freed Rajputana from the fear of famine and thirst forever. Years in the building, they were constructed laboriously, without benefit of dynamite, derricks, or bulldozers, and so their great extent makes them all the more amazing. The massive blocks of marble were raised into position by sheer musclepower—pushed by groaning slaves up inclined ramps of bamboo many miles long, and dropped into place.

These two stunning marble dams of India, though they were built only a moment ago so far as historical time goes, actually hark back to the simplest era of dam-building. For they are nothing but giant barricades to hold back water. Long before they were built, man had learned to find more complex uses for dams.

3

Putting Water to Work

~~~~~~

RUSHING water has great strength. A relatively small stream can slice a mighty channel through solid rock. The mile-deep gash that is the Grand Canyon of the Colorado was cut by waterpower. Anyone who has tried to swim against the current of a vigorous river understands how strong water can be.

Sometime in the dim past, man learned to put water to work for his own uses. He discovered that the strength of a stream could be used to run a mill that would grind grain into flour.

This discovery could have taken place only where manpower was not unlimited. If there were an endless supply of slaves to run the mills, why bother inventing a water-driven mill? Necessity is indeed the mother of invention, and in ancient times few pioneering discoveries were made out of mere idle curiosity.

Thus the first waterpowered mill probably did not originate in Egypt or in Mesopotamia. There, slaves were in ample supply, and the impetus to invent a substitute for them did

not exist. Furthermore, the Nile, the Tigris, and the Euphrates
are not the sort of rivers that are best suited to water-powered
mills. They are irregular in their flow, flooding wildly part
of the year, sluggish the rest. And they are too big for the
purpose. What is needed is a rapidly flowing mountain stream.
The first water wheel was probably devised in the hills of
Iran, or in some other mountainous part of the Near East,
where slaves were few, and weary farmers sought some re-
lief from the endless chore of milling grain with mortar and
pestle.

One escape from manpower is to use animals. In many
parts of the ancient world—and in some primitive regions today—donkeys were used as millhands. The donkey was harnessed to the mill and made to walk round and round, turning the grinder as he went. The invention of the circular mill,
about 2,500 years ago, was a great advance over the technique of pounding grain to free it of its husks.

But even this was not a fully satisfactory method. Donkeys
must be fed; they sicken, grow old, must be replaced. In a
time of plague, the mill animals might perish and deprive a
community of bread just when it would be most needed. Advanced thinkers of the ancient world tried to find some way
of freeing man from this dependency on animal power and
on his own muscle power.

The inventor of the water-wheel mill is known. He was
Marcus Vitruvius Pollo, known as Vitruvius, a Roman archi-
tect who lived in the first century before Christ.

There had been waterpowered mills before Vitruvius—the
so-called Greek mill, which was probably not invented in
Greece at all but somewhere in the Near East. The Greek
mill, still in use in very backward parts of the world, is not
an efficient type of mill, but it does get the job of grinding
done—eventually. Its big advantage is that it is simply constructed and needs no musclepower, animal or human, to operate. A stream does all the work. The Greek mill consists
of a horizontal water wheel set directly down in the bed of
a stream. The stream flows into buckets along the side of the

wheel and causes it to turn. A vertical shaft rising from the
wheel leads to two millstones, one atop the other. The shaft
passes through the bottommost millstone and is fastened to
the topmost one. As the wheel turns, the shaft attached to
the grinding stone turns also, and the grain is milled between
the two stones.

Such a mill works slowly. When the water is sluggish, the
grain is milled sluggishly, since the millstones cannot turn
faster than the water wheel that powers them. But in a stream
that flows swiftly throughout the year, a considerable bit of
milling can be done—far more than by pounding away with
a mortar and pestle, or by compelling hapless donkeys to go
round and round and round.

Vitruvius probably knew about the so-called Greek mill.
But the Vitruvian water wheel was a tremendous engineering
advance over it. He used a *vertical* wheel set in a swiftly
flowing stream. It was of the undershot variety, that is, the
water came rushing toward the wheel and hit buckets at the
bottom of the wheel, causing it to turn. An ingenious system
of cogs geared the wheel to the grindstone via a horizontal
shaft. The result was far more efficient than the rattle-and-
bang Greek mill; the lower buckets were always in water,
and the wheel turned endlessly, generating far more grinding
power than the horizontal wheel lying completely in the water. The easiest way to visualize the Vitruvian mill is to think
of a carnival's Ferris wheel, with its dangling cars. Picture a
stream flowing along and striking the bottommost of the cars.
As the car fills with water, the stream pushes it along; the
next car drops to stream level, is filled, and moves along, and
so on. Car by car, the stream turns the wheel, and if the
wheel is connected by a shaft to grindstones, it can be used
to mill flour.

The Vitruvian, or Roman mill, was slow to gain acceptance.
Reliance on slave labor or on donkeys was easier to accept;
people tend to remain stuck in old ways until the force of
circumstance budges them. But during the early centuries of
the Christian era, Roman mills began to gain more widespread

favor as the institution of slavery declined. By A.D. 500, Roman mills were in general use throughout most of Europe and the Near East.

You must understand that cultural advances do not spread uniformly over the world simultaneously. Even today, with global communications, there are parts of the world where television and automobiles are unknown. In the vastly more fragmented world of 2,000 years ago, new technological developments traveled much more slowly. And so while the Romans used the Vitruvian mill in A.D. 300, the inhabitants of the British Isles were still struggling along with the Greek mill, as were the Chinese, while in Africa and most of Asia donkey-powered mills were still in use. Across the Atlantic in the yet undiscovered New World, the Indians were still pounding their corn by hand, as they would continue to do for many more centuries.

Somewhere between the year A.D. 500 and the year A.D. 1000, another great step forward was taken in the art of putting water to work for man, when the overshot water wheel was invented. This invention probably spread outward from some European country, England or France or the Low Countries. For the banner of civilization had been moving ever westward; the time of Egypt and Mesopotamia had come and gone, Greece and Rome too had flourished and faded, and the new strongholds of human intelligence were the lands of Western Europe.

The overshot wheel mill, unlike the Greek mill or the Roman (Vitruvian) mill, required a mill dam. The Greek mill simply ran in an open stream; the Vitruvian mill could do the same, or it could be run by an aqueduct leading out of a river. Some undershot wheels may have been used with dams, but it was the overshot wheel that made them necessary for milling.

An overshot wheel is also a vertical type wheel with buckets to catch the flowing water. But it stands downstream from a small dam. The dam creates a pond, which backs up behind the dam. The top of the overshot wheel is at the same height as the level of the water in the pond, or is slightly below that height.

A canal—called the millrace—leads from the pond to a wooden chute that conveys water to the top of the wheel. The straining waters of the pond are held back by a gate known as a flume gate. When this gate is lifted, the water rushes from the pond, down the millrace and into the chute, and from there to the topmost bucket of the wheel, which begins to turn under the impact of the water hitting it. The action of the overshot wheel is thus the opposite of the undershot wheel's action. While the undershot wheel turns from the force of the water rushing along the bed of the stream, the overshot wheel is powered by the weight of the water falling into its buckets from above. The extra push imparted by gravity gives the overshot wheel much more power than its earlier competitor.

Thus the third great use of dams came into being. The earliest dams had been used for creating reservoirs for irrigation; next, flood control had been added to the function of the dam. Now, dams began to be used for power.

These mill dams were much smaller than the great irrigation and flood control dams of the ancients. They were built across streams, not rivers, and there was no need for great size. The mill dams were usually constructed of earth, stones, timber, or a combination of the three, piled across the stream bed until the water began to back up. Taken individually, these dams were no colossal feats of engineering. It is only when one looks at them in context, and sees them as part of the intricate and sophisticated mechanism of the overshot wheel mill, that full appreciation of their importance is possible.

Water wheels spread all over Europe, and soon every stream that was near farmland had its own dam and its own busily turning wheel. In some countries, most notably the Netherlands, windmills were preferred, but the principle of harnessing nature's energies to grind wheat was the same.

Water mills came to the New World with the European

settlers. The Indians, though they had an infinity of beavers to serve as preceptors, had built no dams, except in the arid regions of the Southwest and in the Aztec, Inca, and Maya cultures of Central and South America—but these dams were only for irrigation purposes. Grain was pounded by hand throughout the New World.

The settlers lost no time in building mills. The first mill in New England, built in 1623, was a windmill, but water-powered mills soon followed, and with them dams. The first water-powered grinding mill was built in Milton, Massachusetts, in 1634. An industrial center rapidly sprang up around it.

Waterpower could be used not only to grind wheat but to saw timber. Sawmills soon joined flour mills in the growing New England colonies. Every village had its own small dam on its own little brook. It was no longer necessary for the brook to be a particularly swift-flowing one, as required by the undershot wheel; the mill dam served to store up water which was then released by the flume gate with enough energy to turn the wheel.

Today water-powered mills are obsolete, though a few water wheels are kept in working order here and there as museum specimens of an earlier way of life. The mill dam is a thing of the past, too. Milling today is done without the help of direct waterpower.

The age of small mill dams, though, was an important one in man's technological history. It marked the vital transition from musclepower to machine power. From century to century, man was learning how to make nature work for him. Change followed change with incredible speed. The technological advances of the years from A.D. 1000 to A.D. 1800 were greater than all that had been accomplished in five to ten thousand years of human history. But the revolution was only beginning. The age of electricity was dawning—and now technology entered into its era of breathless leapfrogging progress, progress that is still going on at an ever accelerating pace.

ELECTRICITY FROM WATER POWER

Electricity has been one of the great mysteries of the universe. It was known, in the form of lightning, long before it was recognized as a source of power to run the world's industry; and it was harnessed for power a century before men had any real understanding of its nature. All during the 18th and the 19th centuries, men struggled to comprehend the phenomenon of electricity. Although in the long view of history it was but a moment of time from the day in the 17th century when the English experimenter coined the word *electric* to the day in the 19th when the first flickering electric light was turned on, the actual path was a rocky and laborious one whose many twists and turns we have no room to deal with in this book.

The work of men like Galvani, Volta, Ampere, and Faraday —all of them immortalized in the names of units of measure or in electrical terms—had led to an understanding of electricity which, though muddy and incomplete, was sufficient to allow the new force to be put to work. Faraday's electromagnet was the great breakthrough that allowed electricity to become man's servant.

Before Faraday, electricity had been generated in a variety of inefficient ways. William Gilbert had generated it through friction, creating sparks and unusual effects by rubbing a bit of amber with a piece of fur. Pieter van Musschenbroek of Leyden, Holland, in 1746, had developed a way of storing friction-generated energy in a bottle, the Leyden Jar. Benjamin Franklin, a few years later, had made his famous—and dangerous—kite experiment to draw electricity down from the clouds. Alessandro Volta, later in the 18th century, had found that contact between two different metals in the presence of acid would produce electricity, and invented the Voltaic pile, a stack of copper and zinc disks interleaved with pieces of blotting paper moistened with vinegar. He could draw strong, steady electrical current from such a pile, and from a series of cups that produced the same effect.

Early in the 19th century, André Ampere studied the laws of electric current and carried out experiments with wires that had electricity running through them. He found that if he put two wires side by side and sent current flowing through them in the same direction they would tend to draw closer together, though not to touch. When he sent current through two wires in opposite directions, they would repel each other.

Next, Ampere experimentally coiled a wire around an iron bar and ran an electric current through it. To his surprise, the iron became a magnet! The mere presence of an electric current in a wire around it could effect an almost magical change in the bar's properties. When the current was turned off, the bar lost its magnetism until the current flowed once again.

Ampere did not follow up his discovery. It remained for a brilliant young Englishman named Michael Faraday to take the logical next step. Ampere had created a magnet by running an electric current into a wire. Faraday wondered if the opposite could be done: could a magnet be made to produce electric current?

In 1831 he began his experiments with magnets. In October, using a cylindrical bar magnet ¾ of an inch thick and 8½ inches long, he wound 220 feet of copper wire into a spiral coil and brought it into contact with the magnet. Excitedly he discovered that when the magnet approached the coiled wire, an electric current flowed through the wire. When the magnet was at rest, no current was produced. But when it moved back and forth, current flowed in the wire.

Faraday's theory to explain this was incorrect, but no matter. He leaped immediately to practical application of his discovery by building a machine that would produce a steady electric current. He rotated a copper disk between the two poles of a horseshoe magnet, and got a direct current at two rubbing contacts on the disk. This was the first electric generator. Its output was low, and its efficiency was poor, but it yielded a current! It was the world's first dynamo.

While Faraday was carrying out his experiments, an American, Joseph Henry, was working independently along similar lines and reached the same result. But because Faraday published his results first, it is to him, and not to Joseph Henry, that credit has gone for the pioneering step in the generation of electricity.

Faraday moved along to other fields of inquiry, but the electric generator became the subject of exhaustive research and development in the laboratories of different investigators. The basic principle of inducing an electric current with a coil and a magnet remained, but the improvements came fast and frequently, and by 1878 Thomas Edison's bipolar generator nearly doubled the efficiency of the best previous design, making commercial use of electricity practicable. The entire electrical revolution had taken about a generation from Faraday to Edison—a mind-wrenchingly short span of time for such a fantastic flow of events.

The telegraph, the telephone, the electric light—these burst swiftly on a dazzled world. Dynamos generated electricity to turn the wheels of factory equipment, replacing steam boilers and water wheels. Irregularities in current flow made industrial uses of electricity chancy even as late as 1900, but improved generator design soon coped with this problem.

The basic phenomenon of generation of current depends on rotating coils. Turbines are used to keep the coils rotating and the current flowing.

A turbine is a rotary motor whose shaft is turned by a current of steam, air, water, or any other fluid. It is operated on the same principle as the windmill or the water-wheel flour mill. A current of water or of steam, spouting from a fixed nozzle, strikes vanes or buckets or blades on the turbine and forces it to turn. The pioneer steam turbines of the 1880's soon gave way to massive water turbines to drive dynamos.

The age of hydroelectric power was beginning: the age of the big dams.

Just as Vitruvius saw that water power could be used to grind wheat, so did the engineers of the late 19th century realize that the power of rivers could be used to drive turbines that would generate electricity. Of course, rivers had an inconvenient way of being far from centers of industry in many cases, but the development of long-distance high-tension lines handled that problem. Electricity could be generated at remote points and transmitted to the cities where it was needed.

You can see that an entire complex of dovetailing inventions, concepts, and developments was necessary to bring about the era of high dams. Technological progress always moves in wide fronts this way; a single isolated discovery, such as Faraday's work with the electromagnet, leads to a mushrooming constellation of new ideas and developments which must interlock at all points if they are to be workable.

Thus Edison, in 1879, would not have developed his incandescent bulb if he had not, the previous year, perfected a generator that he knew would supply reliable current. So, too, the entire swarming complexity of ideas sprang up as an interdependent structure: generators, turbines, factories, long-distance high-tension lines, and, finally, mighty dams in remote parts of the world.

We have now reached the real beginning of our story. The modern age of dams opens. In the chapters to come, we will see something of the multifarious diversity of 20th-century dams, which are the biggest and perhaps the most complex structures ever built by man.

4

The Age of High Dams

LARGE-SCALE dam-building is not readily suited to private enterprise. It tends to be too expensive. Nowadays even a small dam costs several millions of dollars, and a really huge one can run to a sum that would tax the treasury of even the giant corporations. In our time, therefore, dam-building has been chiefly a government activity. This has led to considerable controversy between the forces of private development and those of public development, as we will see. It is a ticklish argument and one that cannot easily be resolved. There are those who feel that more dams should have been built through private enterprise, and others who believe that every large-scale power project should be undertaken by the Government.

The U.S. Government got into the dam-building business in a big way on June 17, 1902, when President Theodore Roosevelt signed into law the Federal Reclamation Act. As its name implies, this was chiefly concerned with building dams for irrigation and soil-conservation purposes. It established the Bureau of Reclamation as a branch of the Department of the

Interior, and gave it responsibility and funds for building large-scale dams for land reclamation, particularly in the western part of the United States.

A second dam-building agency of the Federal Government was the Corps of Engineers of the U.S. Army. The Army Engineers were first authorized by the Continental Congress in 1775; they were disbanded 8 years later, but in 1802 Congress created a new Corps of Engineers. Among the early responsibilities of the Army Engineers was the operation of the United States Military Academy at West Point, which they ran until 1866. Even today, top-ranking cadets at West Point are nicknamed "engineers."

Early in the 1820's the Army Engineers were given the assignment of maintaining the nation's inland waterways. This involved them in projects to improve navigation on the Mississippi and Ohio Rivers, to build the Chesapeake and Ohio Canal, and to remove shipping hazards on the Missouri River. In 1852 Congress gave them the general assignment of river and harbor maintenance. The year 1917 saw flood control made an official part of the Army Engineers' operations, and the Flood Control Act of 1936 specified that they were to build dams as necessary for the purpose of flood control.

As you might guess from your knowledge of the events in the valley of the Nile, irrigation and flood control do not always fit into totally separate compartments. The same dam may serve as an aid to agriculture and as a check against damaging floods.

Accordingly, the responsibilities of the Bureau of Reclamation and the Army Engineers overlap in a good many places. What is more, the two branches of the Government have not always seen eye to eye in their evaluation of the need for a given project. It is not unknown for the Bureau of Reclamation to favor a dam-building project that the Army Engineers think is impractical or unnecessary, or vice versa.

This has led to a certain amount of friendly and not-so-friendly jockeying back and forth, and also to more than a little confusion about responsibilities. This confusion has been compounded by the changeable views of the Congress of the United States, by the conflict between the supporters of private and public power, and by many other factors, so that the story of dam-building in this country is a tangled and gnarled one.

We will do our best to cut through the underbrush of confusion as we go along. For the time being, let it simply be understood that most of the dam-building is done in this country by the Bureau of Reclamation and the Army Engineers, and that these dams are built for the purpose of irrigation, flood control, hydroelectric power generation, or —most frequently—a combination of the three.

Dams of various shapes and sizes are also being built all the time by other government arms such as the Tennessee Valley Authority and the Soil Conservation Service. Power companies and industrial firms build dams. So do farmers. Cities and states and townships build dams. Hundreds and hundreds of dams dot the countryside, ranging in size from small earth-fill structures and beaver dams to towering piles of reinforced concrete.

ROOSEVELT DAM

One of the first dams to be built under the Reclamation Act of 1902 was Roosevelt Dam, on the Salt River in Arizona. This was something of an engineering landmark in its time, but today it seems more quaint than anything else.

Quaint is possibly an odd word to apply to a stone structure 280 feet high. But the Roosevelt Dam (named for Theodore Roosevelt and not for FDR, who was going to college while it was built) has a cluttered, fussy look about it that looks back toward the Victorian era rather than forward to the slim, sleek dams that have succeeded it on America's rivers.

Roosevelt Dam was begun in 1905 and completed and dedicated early in 1911. It is of the type known as "Solid Masonry Gravity Dam," which simply means that it is made of solid blocks of concrete which hold back the flow of water by sheer weight. This type of dam is one of the most ancient, though of course in the times of the Pharaohs stone and not concrete was used to form the building blocks.

Solid masonry dams of the past had been extraordinarily massive, so that they would not yield to the pressure of the river battering against them. In the 19th century, however, engineering work done by W. J. M. Rankine and others provided a scientific basis for building them. Before that time it had been necessary to build masonry dams whose width was at least three or four times their height. The new developments permitted the building of durable dams which could be higher than they were thick—a vital step forward in efficiency, greatly reducing the job of construction.

The Salt River of Arizona flowed through a desert before Roosevelt Dam was built. Early attempts at dam-building had ended in failure; melting snows in early spring had caused floods that ripped the pioneering dams away. Roosevelt Dam, built in a narrow gorge and supported at each end by natural rock abutments, did the job. It formed a large reservoir which has been used ever since for irrigation.

Roosevelt Dam, as we already mentioned, is not streamlined. Its texture is rough and ridged, and it is topped with towers and battlements that make it look something like a fortress. For all its medieval appearance, though, it achieved its purpose, and reclaimed a vast stretch of desert.

Building the dam was no easy matter. In 1905 there was no trucking industry, and the materials for the dam had to be hauled by mule and horse cart over 112 miles of newly constructed road. The workmen who built this road, and who went on to build the dam afterward, were largely Apache Indians, who had been on the warpath not too many decades earlier.

To provide power for operating the digging and cement-pouring machine, the contractor set up a small hydroelectric plant 20 miles upstream from the site of the dam. To save haulage time, the contractor built a cement mill near the dam site, while a sawmill built in the mountains 30 miles away provided the timber that was needed.

It had originally been expected that the dam would be built in 3 years. As it turned out, 5 were needed, for all manner of special problems were encountered. In order to build a dam, the river must be "turned off" and diverted from its channel in some way, and this is usually done by throwing up a cofferdam, a temporary structure to hold back the waters while the real dam is being built. At the Roosevelt Dam site, the first cofferdam was swept away by a sudden flood almost as soon as it was completed. Grimly the workmen began the grueling job all over again, and the second dam held, though placed under severe stress by a later flood.

Building the 500-foot-long sluicing tunnel for the hydroelectric plant was attended by headaches, too. A rise of only 2 feet in the river's level was enough to flood the tunnel, and this happened three times. Then, too, the workmen kept tapping hot springs under the tunnel's floor. Steaming vapor filled the excavation, driving the men back time and again. For long periods the temperature in the tunnel hovered around 130° Fahrenheit, and the workers stripped almost down to the skin, and had to come up for fresh air at frequent intervals.

Despite all this, the dam was built. When completed, it formed a lake with a capacity of ½ billion gallons of water. Today that lake supplies a ¼ million acres of former desert land with water, piped over 1,000 miles of irrigation canals. The completed dam, 280 feet high, was 158 feet thick and spanned a length of 1,125 feet. Had the dam been built without the benefit of 19th-century engineering advances in design and stress control, it would have had to be 700 to 1,000 feet thick at the base, a far more cumbersome thing to build than a svelte 158-footer.

Roosevelt Dam was rightly acclaimed as the major engineering achievement that it was. Yet this titan of its day was soon to be dwarfed. The Bureau of Reclamation went on to build such vastly greater dams as Hoover Dam (Boulder Dam), the Grand Coulee, Shasta Dam, and Hungry Horse Dam, while the Army Engineers were responsible for the Fort Peck Dam, the Garrison Dam, and hundreds of others.

Five years after the completion of Roosevelt Dam came another major Bureau of Reclamation project, the Arrowrock Dam on the Boise River in Idaho. This was one of many dams to wear the crown of "Highest Dam in the World" for a brief while. Arrowrock, 350 feet high, topped Roosevelt Dam by 70 feet. Today, however, this one-time highest dam is far down the list; many dams are twice its height, and one, the spectacular Vaiont Dam in Italy, completed in 1961, dwarfs Arrowrock by more than 500 feet—the size of a 50-story skyscraper—with a maximum height of 870 feet.

Nor will Vaiont Dam wear its crown for long. The Grand Dixence Dam in Switzerland, which will be completed in 1966, will leave it far behind, attaining the incredible height of 940 feet. And from the Soviet Union comes word of a projected 990-foot dam on the Ingouri River near the city of Volgågrad, more familiar to Westerners under its old name of Stalingrad. The day of the thousand-foot dam is not too far off, we can confidently predict.

Arrowrock, though, was an important achievement in President Wilson's day. A curved concrete dam, it has the slim, modernistic lines of the 20th-century's esthetic ideal, rather than the Victorian look of Roosevelt Dam. By backing up water into the north and south forks of the Boise River, it formed a Y-shaped reservoir 17 miles long.

The Arrowrock Dam has one novel feature worth mention. Because it was built in logging country, it was designed to handle logs. As the felled logs come floating downstream into the reservoir, a cable lifts them out and places them on a platform. From there, a conveyor belt moves them to a chute that spews them out downstream of the dam, where they can continue on their way to the mill. The log-lifter can handle a million feet of lumber a day.

Other large dams of that early period of high dam building include the 301-foot-high Elephant Butte Dam on the Rio Grande in New Mexico, which was completed also in 1916 and which, though shorter than Arrowrock, backs up a reservoir four times as large; Stony Gorge Dam in California, finished in 1928, an "Ambursen" type dam supported by buttresses; and the 295-foot Seminoe Dam in Wyoming, whose 200,000 cubic yards of concrete were placed in a single season despite bleak winter conditions (the construction men worked under canvas to keep warm).

Although there were numerous dams built by the Government between 1905 and 1933, the most exciting era of dambuilding opened when Franklin Delano Roosevelt brought the New Deal to the White House. Roosevelt had an entirely new concept of the role of government in national affairs. While his Republican predecessors, Harding, Coolidge, and Hoover, had followed their party's traditionally cautious ways, Roosevelt expanded the Federal Government's functions dynamically. His philosophy of government involved great expenditures for public works—and that meant dams.

Some of the New Deal's dam-building projects dated from the time of earlier administrations, but though conceived by governments of the pre-New Deal days, they received their greatest backing from the Roosevelt Administration. One of these projects was Hoover Dam, which we will discuss in the next chapter. Though Congress had authorized its construction in 1928, Hoover Dam was constructed mainly during the Roosevelt days.

The biggest and certainly the most controversial of the Roosevelt public-power projects was the Tennessee Valley Authority, which will rate a chapter of its own further on in this book. The nearly a score of dams built in the first decade of the TVA comprised a chain of constructions of almost unparalleled scope, whose combined mass was more than a dozen times that of the Pyramids of Egypt. The TVA went into operation in 1933. Soon afterward, a myriad other projects were under way. By 1936 almost 20 large-scale dams were under construction in the United States. The Army Corps of Engineers was at work building Bonneville Dam on the Columbia River and gigantic Fort Peck Dam on the Missouri. The Bureau of Reclamation, authorized to operate in seventeen western states, was putting the finishing touches on Hoover

Dam (then known as Boulder Dam) and was making the preliminary studies for the new titan to be built on the Columbia River, Grand Coulee Dam.

The Army Engineers and the Bureau of Reclamation were often at cross-purposes during this period, as, indeed, they have been many times since. The traditional role of the Army Engineers was to deal with problems of navigation and flood control, while the Bureau of Reclamation dealt with irrigation problems. In theory, the Bureau of Reclamation would work upstream, the Army Engineers downstream, and there would be no conflict.

But the prevailing philosophy of the new dam-building era was the "multi-purpose" dam. Production of electric power, flood control, and irrigation were made functions of one and the same dam. Thus the old lines of demarcation between the two dam-building agencies became hopelessly blurred, and it was necessary for Congress to allot the assignments to one or the other on less specific grounds than that of simple purpose.

It seemed only logical to include power-producing equipment in the new great dams. The public power argument ran that so long as the dams were needed for flood control and irrigation, why not go to the relatively small additional expense of including generating plants? That way, cheap electric power could be produced to benefit the people of the nation, who were, after all, footing the bill for the construction of the dam.

The attack on this idea came from a number of quarters. Most vehement of all, naturally, were the private power companies, who saw the Government's program as a direct threat to their welfare. They did not want to be forced to compete with the U.S. Government, and saw the Government's entry into power production as a step toward socialism. These private power manufacturers insisted that no public works projects of the sort were really necessary.

"Could anything be more unfair?" asked Thomas N. Mc-Carter, president of the Edison Electric Institute, when the

New Deal's public-power plans were announced. "Could anything be more outrageous? In all these respective localities
there is a far greater abundance of power now existing in the
resources already established other than is needed."

The Army Engineers shared this viewpoint. They felt that
the new public dams should not sell power directly to the
consumers. Instead, they argued, the electricity generated at
the dams should be sold to the private power companies, who
could then resell it to the public. While the Bonneville Dam
was under construction, in 1936, bills were introduced in Congress giving the Army Engineers the right to operate the dam
and to sell its power to anyone they chose—meaning the private
power companies. President Roosevelt opposed this idea, and
in 1937 the Bonneville Power Act was passed, permitting the
public to obtain low-cost electricity directly from the Government.

A second attack on public power came from a segment of
the taxpayers who objected to the whole scheme because it
did not benefit them. A man who lived in Chicago or New
York would not gain from the new dams. *His* electricity rates
would not be lowered. Cheap power in Oregon or Arizona or
Tennessee had no appeal for him. "Why should I be taxed,"
such a man could argue, "so that people in Seattle will pay
less for their electricity?"

This is an argument that arises again and again in a country
so large as this. When the public's money is spent for something that will benefit only one region of the nation, other
regions have a way of objecting. City people grumble over
farm subsidies, country people oppose Federal aid to com-
muter transportation, Easterners are unable to see the need
for new dams in the Far West, and so on.

There are strong arguments on both sides. Many liberals be-
lieved that Roosevelt's campaign to bring cheap power to the
people through public works was of inestimable value to the
entire nation. For example, Arthur Schlesinger, Jr., a pro-New
Deal historian now in the Kennedy Administration, has written
of a single Roosevelt public-power program, the Rural Elec-

trification Administration, "Where farm life had been so recently drab, dark, and backbreaking, it now received in a miraculous decade a new access of energy, cleanliness, and light. No single event, save perhaps for the invention of the automobile, so effectively diminished the aching resentment of the farmers and so swiftly closed the gap between country and city. No single public agency ever so enriched and brightened the quality of rural living."

Schlesinger's discussion of New Deal power philosophy is similarly enthusiastic about the TVA, the Bonneville Power Act, and the rest of the New Deal's electricity-marketing programs. But political conservatives do not share his enthusiasm. For example, Elmer Peterson's book *Big Dam Foolishness*, an attack on dams in general and flood control theory in particular, has this to say about the Federal power program:

"One of the strangest angles in all this complex picture is that you will occasionally find 'dollar socialists' playing important parts. They are infrequent and shortsightedly selfish public utility retailers of power, who antagonize the long-range welfare of their own private enterprise system by whooping it up for big federal power dams. That is because they happen to be in position to buy federal power wholesale at a lower rate than they can produce it themselves or buy it from private wholesalers. Then they sell it at a profit. Naturally this is confusing to the lay public, which is not familiar with all the 'wheels within wheels.'

"The real issue, notwithstanding the complexities, stands out, stark and grim. It is the certainty that growing federal power operations, whether by steam or hydro plant, furnish the line of least resistance to the ambitious politicians who are trying to change our system to a socialist state, many of them without even knowing the basic meanings and techniques of socialism, but knowing only the materialist lure of 'changing the world.'"

These are the two extremes in the public power controversy: the New Dealers who praise the program for its success, in Mr. Schlesinger's words, in stimulating "the use of electricity by lowering the price—to tap markets which the power companies, bound to a narrow faith in quick and certain profits, had thus far been unwilling or unable to open up," and the conservatives, who, like Mr. Peterson, see the whole public power program as part of a plot on the part of those "who are trying to change our system to a socialist state."

The debate has been going on for decades, and shows no sign of reaching a halt. It is important, in the understanding of our dam-building program, to know both points of view, and so they have been presented. The entire problem is far too complex to be summed up in a few quick sentences. Suffice it to say that the U.S. Government is in the power business in a big way, and, for better or for worse, will remain there for the foreseeable future.

5

Hoover Dam

~~~~~~

THE controversy over public versus private power is a serious, philosophical political debate. But politics can be a petty matter, too, as is demonstrated by the silly business of the name of the big dam on the Colorado River, which was once the greatest of all man-made structures and is still well up there in the ranks of the highest, biggest, and mightiest.

The dam now called Hoover Dam was discussed and debated for many years, but the first real step toward getting it off the drawing boards was taken on January 26, 1922, when the Colorado River Commission, appointed by President Harding held its first meeting to discuss the idea of building the dam. The presiding officer at the meeting was Herbert Hoover, then the Secretary of Commerce. The dam was to be called Boulder Dam.

The actual authorization to build the dam was passed by Congress in December 1928. A few months later Herbert

Hoover entered the White House. By order of his Secretary of the Interior, Ray Lyman Wilbur, the name of the dam was changed from Boulder Dam to Hoover Dam.

But in 1933 the Democrats replaced the Republicans in control of the Government. President Roosevelt's Secretary of the Interior, Harold Ickes, felt it was not fitting for the new administration to have to dedicate a dam that was named after an ex-President of the other political party. So in 1933 he ordered the name changed back to Boulder Dam, and thus it was known for 14 years. It was dedicated under that name in 1936, and most people who went to school in the 1930's and 1940's still tend to think of it as Boulder Dam.

In 1946, however, the Republicans gained control of Congress, and the following year they put through a bill changing the name of the dam back to Hoover Dam. Hoover Dam it remains.

Hoover Dam was a political problem in other ways, too, and much more serious ways. The difficulty lay in deciding who was to benefit from the dam, and to what extent.

The big dam straddles the Colorado River, which rises in the state for which it is named, and runs down through Utah and into Arizona, forming the boundary between that state and first Nevada, then California, emptying finally into the Gulf of California in Mexico.

The Colorado is a river with muscles. It is not much to look at—a fairly narrow stream in many places, hardly more than a trickle in times of drought. And it is muddy—"too thick to drink, too thin to plough."

The mud should be some indication of how strong a river the Colorado is. As it flows southward out of the Rockies, it flays the land, carving out steep canyons, carrying tons and tons of mud and silt along with it. The mile-deep walls of the Grand Canyon testify to the power of the river. Many a tourist has made the long mule ride down the walls of the Grand Canyon, only to peer over the rim at the river below and to be disappointed by its mud-brown color and its seemingly insignificant size.

The Colorado is a young river. It flows down a steep gradient, cutting as it goes. Sometime in the far future, it will "mature" as a river, after it has cut a level channel for itself. Then it will flow along placidly, like the Hudson River in New York, no longer carving out canyons. Young rivers are the most turbulent, the fastest-flowing, the deepest-digging. And they are the best sources of hydroelectric power.

In the 19th century, when the Colorado was first discovered, the idea of building dams to get hydroelectric power was unheard of, and it did not seem that the Colorado River was good for anything at all. Major John W. Powell, who in 1869 led the first expedition to successfully navigate the Colorado, barely made it through the treacherous rapids alive. Hidden fangs of rock made the Colorado deadly for boats; though many expeditions have traveled Major Powell's route in the last century, it is still a trip for daredevils only. Certainly the Colorado has little value for commercial shipping.

Nor was it of much value for agriculture. The very vigor of the river's descent had cut so deep a canyon that none of its water could aid the surrounding land, and so it flowed through an almost uninhabited desert for most of its run. Only near the river's mouth, down by the Mexican border, were the canyon walls low enough so that water could be carried out by canal to irrigate the valleys bordering on the river.

In 1896 an outfit called the California Development Company began to build irrigation canals that would carry water from the lower Colorado River to the nearby Imperial Valley, which was fertile but short of rain. The efforts of the California Development Company were hampered, however, by a maddening feast-or-famine situation. Much of the year, the Colorado was simply too puny to provide much of an irrigation supply. Then, after the spring thaws, the river became a raging monster, roaring out of the Rockies and flooding the canals. Irrigation was not very practicable under such circumstances, since the outer farms of the Imperial Valley did not get enough water during the dry season, while the farms nearest the river were regularly drowned every spring.

To combat this unattractive dilemma, the California Development Company's engineers built dikes, or levees, which they hopefully thought might hold back the floods. This would not solve the problem of the droughts, but at least it would keep back the destructive springtime torrents. Or so they hoped. But the runaway river was not so easily tamed. As fast as levees were built, the river deposited silt in the canals, so that the water level was always on the rise. The canals filled with muck and debris carried down from the north.

Spring floods in 1904 worked enormous damage. When the flood waters receded, engineers dug a bypass channel running alongside the silted-up Imperial Canal, the idea being to provide a diversion channel to handle next spring's floods. Unfortunately, the flooding season was not quite over. Fresh torrents came hurtling downstream before a gate could be built across the gap between the canal and the bypass. The water flooded into the bypass and then on into the Imperial Canal, and spilled on out over the farmlands of the Imperial Valley, surging onward until it reached a depressed area, 280 feet below sea level, then known as the Salton Sink. Since that year, the Salton Sink has been the Salton Sea—a lake of 300 square miles formed by the 1904 flood.

It took several years and a good many millions of dollars to wrestle the river out of this new channel that led to the Salton Sea, and back into the old bed that led to the Gulf of California. Finally the levees were restored, but in 1909 the demonic river broke loose again, creating still another new channel. This time, luckily, the flood waters reached the Gulf of California anyway, but not before doing considerable damage en route.

The Okerson Levee restored the original river channel in 1910. The river broke through it contemptuously almost at once. Another catastrophe occurred in 1916, when the Gila River, a tributary of the Colorado, sent a massive avalanche of water downstream, 200,000 cubic feet per second. The town of Yuma, Arizona, where the Gila empties into the Colorado, was flooded to a depth of 4 feet.

Taming this wildcat of a river was obviously desirable—but how? What could restrain these terrible floods? How could the raging water of the Colorado be held back and stored, to be used for irrigation in time of drought, and for electric power throughout the year?

A dam had to be built, clearly. But simply saying there ought to be a dam was a long hop from actually getting out and building one. Damming the Colorado was no light task, and those who suggested doing it were looked upon as wild visionaries and dreamers.

The archdreamer of them all was a man named Arthur Powell Davis. He was the son of the sister of Major John Powell, the colorful, one-armed Civil War veteran who in 1869 made that suicidal 90-day trip down the Colorado through the majestic Grand Canyon. Arthur Davis was 8 years old when his uncle made that heroic journey, and he was deeply impressed by his uncle's tales of adventure—especially when Major Powell expressed his hope that the wild fury of the Colorado could someday be harnessed for the benefit of mankind, and his conviction that the job would eventually be done.

How splendid it would be, young Davis thought, if he could be instrumental in taming this demon of a river! His uncle had conquered it by boat—but could the river be brought under control permanently? Arthur Davis thought it could be.

In 1914 Arthur Davis became director of the U.S. Bureau of Reclamation. One of his first acts was to present a plan for damming the Colorado. At that time, the highest dam in the world was only about 300 feet high. French engineers were working on one that they thought of as a colossus—450 feet high. But the dam that Arthur Davis envisioned would have to be as high as both those dams *together*—at least 700 to 750 feet!

It was an ambitious plan. Behind the incredibly high walls of this gargantuan dam, a reservoir would slowly fill up in the canyon of the Colorado, a reservoir big enough to hold every drop of water the Colorado could send along in any 2 years of steady flow. It would be the biggest man-made lake in the world, holding enough water to cover New York State to a depth of 1 foot, or Connecticut to a depth of 10. Water from this reservoir would generate 6 billion kilowatt-hours of electrical energy each year for the growing cities of Southern California. The reservoir would hold the flood waters as they came spilling down, and the spillways of the dam would release the water in measured amounts, to continue in tranquillity down to the farmlands of the Imperial Valley.

Flood control, hydroelectric power, irrigation—the proposed dam on the Colorado was to be a multipurpose dam, a three-way guardian of the Southwest. In addition to these main purposes, there were others: the dam would provide a supply of drinking water for thirteen Californian cities, and it would create, in its reservoir, a recreation area that would be navigable for many miles.

When Arthur Davis proposed this grandiose scheme, he was met by scoffers of all sorts. "It'll cost a fortune," some said. "Who wants to spend all that money just to dam up a wild river off in a part of the country nobody lives in?"

Others solemnly maintained that the dam could not be built at all. The wild Colorado would not stand still long enough to permit puny men to throw a wall across her gullet. Still others were willing grudgingly to admit that the dam might be built, but not that it would last. "It'll be swept away by the first big flood. Let that reservoir build up, and when the dam goes it'll wipe out half of California."

The pessimists had a field day. One morbid school held that raising and lowering of the level of water in the reservoir would strain the Earth's surface and cause earthquakes; the San Francisco quake of 1907 was still recent enough to give everyone the feeling that the entire Southwest was likely to erupt and slide into the Pacific at any moment, especially if fancy dams were built. And some shortsighted observers, unable to foresee the mushrooming growth of Los Angeles and the cities around it, asked balefully where the customers would come from to buy the 6 billion kilowatt-hours of energy that the new dam would produce.

Undaunted by all this, the Bureau of Reclamation went

ahead. The next step was to survey the Colorado and decide on the best site for the dam.

The Colorado River has two natural basins, the Upper and the Lower. The states drained by the waters of the Upper Basin are Wyoming, Colorado, Utah, New Mexico, and Arizona. The Lower Basin states are Arizona, New Mexico, Nevada, Utah, and California.

Building the dam in the Upper Basin would not, therefore, be very helpful so far as supplying California's Imperial Valley with water or Los Angeles with electric power was concerned. The dam had to be built in the Lower Basin, and the Bureau of Reclamation's engineers roamed the spectacular gorges of the Colorado, seeking the best possible site.

They studied 70 in all before choosing Black Canyon, on the border between Arizona and Nevada, 30 miles from the city of Las Vegas, Nevada. Here the river winds through perpendicular reddish-black cliffs 1,000 feet high, 2,000 feet in some places. At the water line the rock walls were 350 feet apart.

The preliminary survey of Black Canyon lasted 3 years. Engineers roamed its sun-baked walls, testing the rock, drilling into it to make certain that it could stand to bear the burden of the enormous weight of concrete that would be laid upon it. Their conclusion was that it could. They recommended that the giant dam be built.

But before the go-ahead could be flashed, important political problems had to be settled. It appeared to the states through which the Colorado flowed that California would be getting the lion's share of the benefits from the intended dam. The Upper Basin states feared that the Lower Basin states, particularly California, would get more than their share of the water of the Colorado, which, after all, flowed through their territory on its way downstream to the site of the proposed dam. The Lower Basin states, in turn, were fearful that the Upper Basin states might divert so much of the river's water that there would not be enough for the benefit of the Lower Basin regions.

The wrangle jeopardized the entire Black Canyon Dam

project. President Harding appointed Herbert Hoover, the
Secretary of Commerce, to a commission which also included
representatives of each of the seven states involved, and in a
series of meetings in 1922, an agreement was reached dividing
the waters of the Colorado between the Upper and Lower
Basins.

Under this agreement, the Upper Basin regions (parts of
Colorado, Utah, Wyoming, New Mexico, and Arizona) were
permitted to divert 7.5 million acre-feet of water each year
for "beneficial consumptive" uses. (An acre-foot is the amount
of water needed to cover 1 acre to a depth of 1 foot.) However, these states—excluding Arizona—are bound not to cause
the flow of the river to drop below a total of 75 million acre-
feet at a specified checkpoint, Lee's Ferry, Arizona, for any
period of 10 consecutive years. When the water drops below
the agreed-on level, the Upper Basin states must curtail their
diversion of water.

The Lower Basin states were also given the right to have
"beneficial consumptive" use of 7.5 million acre-feet of water
per year, with the right to increase their consumption by 1
million acre-feet a year. Later on, the U.S. Government signed
a treaty with Mexico guaranteeing that country 1.5 million to
1.7 million acre-feet of water per year, since the Colorado
also flows through Mexican territory on its way to the sea.

The division of waters between the Upper and Lower Basins solved at least the largest problem, and construction of
the dam could begin. But the individual states in the two
basins had difficulties apportioning their allotment of water
among themselves. It took the Upper Basin states until 1948
to agree on individual water rights, while the Lower Basin
states are still in disagreement on the matter.

This is causing continued friction in the Southwest. For example, in 1952 and 1953 the U.S. Senate twice approved the
Central Arizona Project, a plan to give Arizona an additional
1.2 million acre-feet of Colorado River water a year. The opposition of California to this idea was so vehement that both
times the measure failed in the House of Representatives. The

water is wanted for additional irrigation on land already under cultivation. Arizona claims that without this water, the irrigated area will lose much of its productive capacity, and that thousands of acres have already been lost. California, though, with an eye toward its own future needs for water, is not minded to let Arizona have any more than it is now getting. The supply is not infinite, after all, mighty as the Colorado River may be.

These are some of the political quarrels that grind on endlessly in regions where great dams are built. All the states of the Southwest are growing rapidly, and no state is willing to part with a drop of water more than it absolutely has to yield to its neighbors.

The apportionment agreed on by the Colorado River Commission clarified the situation enough to allow construction to begin. In December 1928 Congress voted an appropriation of $165,000,000 for construction of what was then named Boulder Dam and for the building of an 80-mile-long canal through southern California, the All-American Canal, to bring the waters of the Colorado to the Imperial Valley.

BUILDING HOOVER DAM

It was not until late 1930 that real work began on the construction of the dam. Herbert Hoover, himself an engineer, was President then. Arthur Powell Davis, 70 years old and about to retire, saw his lifelong dream fulfilled as he stood high above the Colorado and watched thousands of workmen toiling with picks and dynamite far below.

Anyone who has visited Las Vegas, that neon-lit capital of the gambling industry, has a pretty fair idea of what the weather is like in that part of the country. During the day, the temperature hovers around the 100° mark much of the year. It is a dry heat, but stifling all the same. Much of the land is desert—flat, gray, depressing desert. It is not a congenial place to build a dam.

Inhospitable as the countryside might have been, a dam had to be built. First, though, a town was built, to house the workmen—the town of Boulder City, built by the Federal Government at a cost of $70,000,000. Boulder City was not allowed to be a collection of temporary shanties, to be thrown up haphazardly and abandoned when the construction job was done. Instead, it was deliberately conceived as a permanent settlement, where, after the construction workers had moved along, the thousands of maintenance workers to be employed by the dam would reside. The 300-acre town, big enough to house 5,000 workers and their families, is notably unlike the pioneer towns of the "wild West." Its neatly laid-out streets are more reminiscent of some cozy suburb than of a Western city built in the desert.

As always, the engineers' initial task was to "turn the river off," to divert its flow while construction was taking place. They dug 4 tunnels, each one 56 feet wide and 4,000 feet long, into the solid rock of the canyon walls. These bypass tunnels would receive the flow of the river and carry it downstream to a point beyond the construction site. Some one and a half million cubic feet of rock had to be removed in building these four bypasses.

Then the cofferdam was built, the temporary restraining wall upstream of the construction site. A gigantic pile of rocks and earth was heaped up, forcing the river into the four bypass tunnels. For the first time in untold eons, the bed of the river was laid bare, exposed to the sun and the air.

Workmen now descended into this drying bed to lay the foundations for the dam. Seven million tons of concrete had to be laid down, in volume amounting to 3,400,000 cubic yards—enough to build a 16-foot-wide road 2,700 miles long, or just about clear across the country. In order to support this staggering burden, as well as the additional burden of the water, the dam had to be 660 feet thick at its base.

Hoover Dam is of the solid concrete gravity type, as was Roosevelt Dam. Both dams curve upstream so that the water load is held back in part by the walls of the canyon. At Hoover, the water exerts a pressure of 45,000 pounds per square inch at the base, and, mighty as the dam is, it needs assistance from the canyon walls to withstand that eternal outward push.

Upward the dam rose, in the shape of a giant fan. As it climbed, it had to grow in length as well, since the V-shaped canyon widened at its rim. Up the concrete mass sprang, past the 500-foot mark, to 600 feet, to 700. At 726 feet above the riverbed, it halted. At that point, the dam spanned 1,300 feet from rim to rim of the canyon, and was less than a tenth of its base thickness, only some 45 feet.

When this great white monster reached its allotted height and spanned the gorge from canyon wall to canyon wall, the construction job was done. It had taken 2 years of nonstop work, *every minute of the day,* 24 hours a day and 365 days a year. Christmas, New Year's, the Fourth of July—the pouring of the concrete had gone on inexorably, under searing desert sun by day, under powerful floodlights at night.

With the job done, the buckets, each holding 16 tons of concrete, could be sent away, the cables cut down, the derricks and trucks and electric shovels retired. The river could flow again. The bypasses were blocked up, and a wall of water came rushing downstream after more than 2 years of confinement.

This is always an unnerving moment in dam-building. Even the most confident of engineers inevitably feels a moment's tingle of irrational panic as he sees his creation about to face the ultimate test. Will it hold? Or will all the calculations and all the years of backbreaking toil go for nothing? Just as the shipbuilder has nightmares of a grand new ocean liner sliding down the runway and immediately nosing down to the depths, so too does the dam-building engineer have cold sweats in the small hours of the morning at the thought of the day when his dam is first called on to do the job for which it is built.

Such irrational fears hardly ever are justified. Dams generally hold.

Boulder Dam held.

The helplessly blockaded waters hit the smooth concrete

wall and stopped there. During the time of construction, the headwaters back of the cofferdam had risen 50 feet despite the bypasses. Now, with the bypasses blocked, the water began to rise much faster, and a lake started to form upstream of the dam.

It took 3 years for the lake—named Lake Mead, after the Commissioner of the Bureau of Reclamation at that time—to reach its desired size. Eventually it backed up a reservoir 115 miles long. Lake Mead is the largest manmade lake in the world, at least at present, though its pre-eminence will be challenged when several dams now under construction are complete.

Today Hoover Dam is one of the great tourist attractions of the Southwest. Buses leave daily from Las Vegas, rolling out into the scorching desert, passing through miles of sagebrush, and suddenly turning into the dam area. A visitor museum helpfully offers an understanding of what the dam is and how it works, but few stop there until they have seen the dam.

A road leads across the very top of the dam. You can walk out on it, and, turning to your left, you look upstream to see the blue majesty of Lake Mead stretching northward for its 115-mile length. The lake may be dotted with pleasure boats far in the distance, since it is now a public recreation area, with beaches, campsites, marinas, and other facilities for the public. Where once an ornery river twisted through steep canyon walls, a placid lake now holds sway, serene and mighty, with enough fish in its 600-foot depths to keep an armada of fishermen happy forever. The old walls of the canyon can still be seen jutting up to frame the lake in reddish-black majesty.

And then you look the other way, and you look down. Far down. Your eye travels down an outward-sloping sweep of beautiful white concrete, and you see the river far below, continuing its flow down toward the Gulf of California. Hundreds of feet below are the powerhouses, which look tiny though they are the size of 20-story skyscrapers.

Hungry Horse Dam, Montana. This is one of the largest dams in the
Columbia River Basin.

Courtesy, Bureau of Reclamation

Canyon Ferry Dam, Montana. View of the downstream face of Canyon Ferry Dam. Water is shown falling through two gates of the spillway. To the left of the photo is the powerhouse and substation.

Courtesy, Bureau of Reclamation

Shasta Dam, California. This giant concrete gravity type dam is located on the Sacramento River. It helps irrigate California's Central Valley and prevents the salt water of the Pacific from ruining San Joaquin Valley.

Courtesy, Bureau of Reclamation

Hoover Dam, Arizona–Nevada. This mighty structure—once known as Boulder Dam—straddles the Colorado River. It is a concrete gravity dam and is one of the great tourist attractions of the Southwest.

Grand Coulee Dam, Washington. The most massive concrete structure in the world, this dam taps the Columbia River, bringing power and water for irrigation to the Pacific Northwest.

Courtesy, Bureau of Reclamation

Detroit Dam, Oregon. Situated on the North Santiam River, its maximum height, foundation to deck, is 191 feet. The Detroit Dam has many uses including flood control, irrigation, navigation, and pollution abatement.

Courtesy, U.S. Army Engineer Division, North Pacific Corps of Engineers

Lookout Point Dam, Oregon. Located on the Middle Fork Willamette River, Lookout Point Dam is an earth and gravel fill unit with a concrete spillway.

Courtesy, Official Corps of Engineers, Portland District

Fort Gibson Dam, Oklahoma. An aerial view of the dam and the power plant is shown. It is located on the Grand (Neosho) River and its main purpose is flood control and power production.

Bull Shoals Dam, Arkansas. Located on the White River, this concrete gravity dam is 258 ft. high and 2256 ft. long. It was completed in 1957.

Courtesy, U.S. Army

Gavins Point powerhouse and spillway is located on the Nebraska side of the two-state project built by Army Engineers on the Missouri River.

Courtesy, U.S. Army, Corps of Engineers, Omaha District

Fort Randall Dam, South Dakota. This huge earth fill dam is one of the key dams in the chain of Missouri River multiple-purpose developments. It was opened on March 15, 1954, by former President Dwight D. Eisenhower.

Norris Dam, Tennessee. This huge dam, built as part of the TVA project, is 265 ft. high and 1860 ft. long. Its reservoir has a storage capacity of two and a half million acre-feet of water.

Cherry Creek Dam, Colorado. Here is a close-up showing the completed intake structure. Water flows into the slender reinforced-concrete intake towers, whose electrically operated gates control the passage of the water onward into the plate-steel pipes. The power of the spurting water drives the giant vertical hydraulic turbines.

Courtesy, U.S. Army, Corps of Engineers, Omaha District

Spiral stairway in the intake tower of Hills Creek Dam on the Middle Fork Willamette River, in Oregon, presents this picture. The tower is as high as a seventeen-story building.

Her Majesty, the Queen, is shown here addressing the gathering assembled at the center of the St. Lawrence Power Project prior to unveiling the International Boundary Marker, June 27, 1959. On the Queen's right are former Vice-President Richard Nixon and Mrs. Nixon. Seated behind Mrs. Nixon is Governor Nelson Rockefeller.

Courtesy, Ontario Hydro

An aerial view is shown, looking upstream at the St. Lawrence Power and Seaway Project near Massena, New York. This ambitious project took four years and more than a billion dollars to complete.

Courtesy, Power Authority of the State of New York

The Iroquois Dam spans the area between Point Rockway in the U.S. (right) and Iroquois Point in Canada. In the lower foreground is the end of the Iroquois Lock, one of the seven newly forged links in the International Seaway chain.

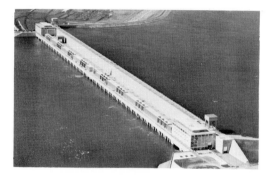

Canadian and U.S. St. Lawrence powerhouses, shown here, were built jointly by Ontario Hydro & the Power Authority of New York State at an estimated cost of $600 million. They have a combined capacity of 1,800,-000 kilowatts.

The graceful arc of the Long Sault Dam thrusts a long finger from the New York State mainland to a point near the head of Barnhart Island. Located three miles upstream from the powerhouse (upper left center), this dam plays an important part in the control of the waters for the headpond of the St. Lawrence Power Project.

A vertical view of Glen Canyon Dam and Powerplant is shown from a point on the west rim approximately one-half mile downstream. At this point, the dam contained nearly 1,950,000 cubic yards of concrete.

Courtesy, Bureau of Reclamation

Work proceeds on the Glen Canyon Dam, part of the Colorado River Storage Project, which is expected to open in 1964. Although the dam is located in Arizona, its big reservoir will be a recreation area in the state of Utah.

Courtesy, Bureau of Reclamation

Looking upstream at Glen Canyon. Steel parts of the dam were raised into position by a motor crane. At the peak of construction, work on the dam kept 22,000 workmen busy.

Courtesy, Bureau of Reclamation

A view of the construction looking over the arch of the Glen Canyon Dam toward the west side of the canyon. To supply the concrete for this project, a concrete plant was built on a ledge hewn out of the canyon wall.

Courtesy, Bureau of Reclamation

Garrison Dam and Reservoir Project, North Dakota. Located on the Missouri River, this dam has been recently completed. Aerial view shows Garrison Dam and lower section of reservoir taken from position downstream and slightly to the right of the spillway pilot channel.

John H. Kerr Dam, Virginia. Located on the Roanoke River, this concrete dam is 144 ft. in length. Its reservoir holds 83,200 acres at flood control pool level in the states of Virginia and North Carolina.

The dam's hydroelectric facilities are open for inspection. First you can look out at Lake Mead and see the four intake towers, 390 feet high, jutting into the lake. Then you can descend, in an elevator that goes right down through the heart of the dam, and visit the powerhouses. The elevator ride is somehow a disturbing one, for you know that leaping, straining masses of water are only a matter of yards from you. You feel a sense of apprehension at the fragility of man and his works. But it gives way, as you continue to descend, to a new feeling of exhilaration and confidence, as you realize that the dam will protect you after all. You feel sudden wonder at the knowledge that small weak creatures very much like yourself somehow succeeded in damming this potent river. By the time you reach the bottom of the shaft, you feel like a giant, holding back the rush of water yourself with one contemptuously outstretched hand!

A tour at the bottom gives you some idea of how the dam functions. You are told how water flows into the slender reinforced-concrete intake towers, whose electrically operated gates control the passage of the water onward into the plate-steel pipes, 30 feet in diameter, set in concrete-lined tunnels. Giant vertical hydraulic turbines are driven by the power of the spurting water as it sluices through to them via penstocks, or regulating gates. As the curved vanes of a turbine are hit by the falling water, the turbine turns, powering the generator. The biggest of these turbines can develop 145,000 horsepower. On and on the turbines whirl, while the river howls like the imprisoned titan that it is, and millions of kilowatts of energy are generated and sent out to light the sparkling blaze of Hollywood.

The power plant covers 10 acres in 2 wings, one along either side of the river, with a connecting structure completing a *U* at the base of the dam. Offices, workshops, and maintenance plants occupy this structure, as well as the power-generating plant.

Only part of the Colorado's water is used for hydroelectric power. The overflow is discharged through outlets high above the powerhouse, and spurts out, 200 feet through the air, in 8-foot-thick jets. Alongside the river are the spillways, two of them, 650 feet long and 150 feet wide. These are for flood control. When high water comes along, the spillways capture it and shoot it through the old bypass tunnels left over from construction days. The flood waters are thus carried off without any danger that they will spill over the crest of the dam. When heavy floods are expected, a further flood control measure is provided by drawing down the waters of Lake Mead. The river beyond the dam is given an additional measure of water, lowering the reservoir level in anticipation of the new rush of floodwater.

This was necessary, for instance, in 1952, when spring thaws were heavy and the Colorado River was flowing strong and fast. To meet the expected abundance of water, power production was boosted at the dam, using more of Lake Mead's water than usual and so drawing down the level of the reservoir. The partly empty reservoir accepted the floodwaters without difficulty, reducing a flow of 122,000 cubic feet per second to one of only 31,000 feet.

The Imperial Valley is also protected by a whole series of further dams downstream from Hoover. These give a guarantee of safety to the region regardless of any conceivable flood conditions. The first of this series of dams, Davis Dam, is about 67 miles downstream of Hoover, in Pyramid Canyon. Built in 1949, Davis Dam forms a reservoir called Lake Mohave, which holds some 1,800,000 acre-feet of water. During flood times, this reservoir level can be lowered by 200,000 acre-feet, thus making room for the extra water that Hoover will be sending downstream.

Further along the course of the river is Parker Dam, built in 1938. Parker Dam has one particular claim to fame that is not readily apparent to the eye. It rises only 85 feet above the riverbed, and so seems to be quite an ordinary dam. But it continues another 235 feet down into the floor of the river, making it 320 feet high in all. It has the deepest submerged section of any dam in the world.

Parker Dam has two main purposes. One is to serve as a flood control dam at times when the storage facilities of Hoover Dam, and of the newer Davis Dam, are sorely taxed. Parker is also used to provide drinking water for the cities of Southern California. As the water travels downstream from Hoover Dam, it picks up a heavy load of silt and sediment. Much of this is skimmed off at Davis Dam, but some continues onward, and more is added. Havasu Lake, the 716,000 acre-foot reservoir formed by Parker Dam, is used as a settling basin where this load of silt is once again dropped, and silt-free water is pumped out and sent onward to Southern California's water system.

Still another dam in this complex series on the lower Colorado River is Imperial Dam, also built in 1938. Imperial, 46 feet high, has a small reservoir, but its main purpose is to serve as a diversion dam that heads the waters of the Colorado into the Gila Valley and All-American irrigation canals.

Imperial Dam is equipped with desilting devices that purify the water of sediment before it heads out for the fields. Before this desilting works went into operation, it cost more than a million dollars a year to keep the two irrigation canals free of silt, so Imperial Dam is a considerable moneysaver.

Upstream of the dam, a trashrack 200 yards long picks up the heavy debris that has entered the water since it left Parker Dam's spillways. Then the water, still laden with fine silt, passes through gates into desilting basins. Here, 125-foot-long scrapers collect the silt and feed it into a trench, where it is piped out and back into the river downstream of the dam. Meanwhile, the silt-free water is diverted into the two canals, 2,000 cubic feet per second into the Gila Gravity Main Canal heading for the farms of Arizona, and about eight times as much into the All-American Canal, California bound.

It can be seen that the job of taming a river like the Colorado cannot be handled by just one dam, even a colossus like Hoover Dam. Rather, teams of dams are employed, each one playing its own part in the over-all scheme of river control.

This is the "afterbay-forebay" system. A forebay is a dam upstream of a big primary dam; an afterbay is a dam downstream of one. Hoover Dam has three afterbays—Davis Dam, Parker Dam, Imperial Dam. They work as a quartet to provide power, water, and flood control for the Lower Basin of the Colorado. Hoover Dam performs the big job of penning up the river. The afterbays have their share in flood control and in power generation, and also play their role in irrigation and silt removal.

Even with this team of dams at work, the Colorado River still was not yielding all the benefits it might have. The Upper Basin still remained wild and turbulent, offering nothing of use to man save its spectacular beauty. Therefore, it was decided to create a second system of dams in the Upper Basin, centering on a primary dam nearly as big as Hoover—the Glen Canyon Dam. We will return to this dam, and to the job of mastering the Colorado River, in a later chapter.

6

Uncle Sam Tames
the Tennessee

~~~~~~
~~~~~~

WHILE the construction of Hoover Dam was going on in the Far West, the attention of the nation turned eastward, to the valley of the Tennessee River, where, in 1933, President Roosevelt urged the building of a truly stupendous series of dams and power plants. The Tennessee Valley Authority came into being through an act of Congress on May 18, 1933. In the generation that has passed, the TVA has built a network of dams and related structures that staggers the mind. Not since the Pyramids of Egypt has there been a similar unified effort of construction.

The message that President Roosevelt sent to Congress called for "a corporation clothed with the power of government but possessed of the flexibility and initiative of a private enterprise. It should be charged with the broadest duty of planning for the proper use, conservation, and development of the natural resources of the Tennessee River drainage basin and its adjoining territory for the general social and economic welfare of the nation."

From the day of its birth, the TVA has been a focal point of argument. Since it represents the Federal Government's most extensive public works program, it has been attacked again and again by conservatives as "socialistic." Private power companies have been most strenuous in the attack, since the TVA supplies low-cost power to the people of the valley.

The one place where the rights and wrongs of the TVA idea are not debated is in the Tennessee Valley itself. There, the new prosperity that came with the dams is the greatest argument in favor of the TVA. The shipping industry on the river is more than 70 times as active as it was in 1933. Flood danger is almost a fading memory today. Barren, eroded land has been turned into fertile farms. Life is vastly different in the Tennessee Valley today, thanks to the dams, and there are few in the region who would wish to undo what has been done.

The Tennessee River had been—in the words of one of the first TVA administrators, David E. Lilienthal—"an idle giant and a destructive one." Five mountain streams feed it—the French Broad, the Holston, the Hiwassee, the Little Tennessee, and the Clinch. They flow together near Knoxville, Tennessee, to form the main body of the river, which then travels in a great westward-moving crescent, dipping southward out of the Appalachians, cutting across the upper third of Alabama, then turning northward again through western Tennessee and the flat fields of Kentucky, to deliver its waters to the Ohio, which carries them on into the Mississippi and thence to the Gulf of Mexico.

The scooping crescent of the Tennessee runs some 650 miles from its source near Knoxville to its meeting with the Ohio not far from Paducah, Kentucky. Seven Southern States are touched by the river or its tributaries, and so form part of the Tennessee Valley drainage area—the western reaches of Virginia and North Carolina, the northern segments of Georgia, Alabama, and Mississippi, and the western half of Kentucky, as well as the whole of the state of Tennessee. The Tennessee Valley embraces geographical extremes, from the high wooded mountains of the Great Smokies in the east to the broad, flat plains of Kentucky in the west. The Valley's area is about equal to that of England and Scotland. Its population today is upward of 10,000,000.

It has always been a growing area, even before the dams came. The State of Tennessee had only 35,691 inhabitants at the time of the first census in 1790, 105,602 a decade later, 1 million by 1850, 2 million by 1900, 3½ million in 1960. The river served as the main highway from town to town, with roads leading off as crossways into the hills and plains.

But one big obstacle, and a host of little ones, interfered with proper development of the Tennessee Valley. The big obstacle was a 37-mile stretch of the river in Alabama that dropped 134 feet in a fairly short span. Rapids, pools, and exposed rocks made this stretch, known as Muscle Shoals, an obstacle to navigation.

As early as 1824 the Federal Government was recommending a canal around the shoals to permit navigation. The State of Alabama built such a canal, with 17 locks, opening it in 1834. Later the Federal Government paid for the enlargement of the canal. Even so, navigation through the canal was not always feasible. Most of the money that went into the various canal-building projects was simply wasted. As the Army Engineers stated in a report in 1916, "It has been impracticable to establish reliable through navigation or even an uninterrupted local navigation extending over any of the reaches."

Building a dam at Muscle Shoals, the Engineers said, would ease the situation. No longer would jagged boulders block shipping. No longer would wild floods turn the river into a raging fury.

A private company had been given a charter to build a Muscle Shoals Dam in 1899, but had never seen the project past the design stage. In 1906, a different company asked the Government to share the costs of building a dam there, but President Theodore Roosevelt turned the idea down, feeling that such an expenditure of Federal money on the behalf of a private company would not benefit the taxpayers at large.

The Muscle Shoals project went into cold storage, and remained there until the outbreak of World War I. Suddenly the United States needed a dependable supply of nitrates, to be used in explosives. Manufacture of nitrates then involved the use of tremendous quantities of power. The National Defense Act of 1916 authorized the President to construct dams, locks, powerhouses, and anything else necessary for the generation of power for the production of nitrates. The Act specified that the nitrate works and power plants were to be operated solely by the Government.

The Army Engineers studied the site and recommended a combined power and navigation site involving three dams, one large one and two smaller ones. Two nitrate plants were built, but neither contributed much to the war effort. The first was a failure from the start, the other was woefully inefficient.

The war ended before anything could be accomplished in the way of building the proposed dams at Muscle Shoals. In November 1917, the first appropriations were made for building of the big dam, now called Wilson Dam. By 1921, with the job about one third done, the money ran out, and it was a year before Congress provided more. Wilson Dam was finally completed in September 1925, at an over-all cost of $47,000,-000. It had eight hydroelectric units with a capacity of 184,000 kilowatts, and space provided for the installation of ten more.

Wilson Dam was called "Dam Number Two" in the Army Engineers' original three-dam project. "Dam Number One," a small navigation dam upstream of Wilson Dam, was completed in 1926. "Dam Number Three," also upstream and intended to supplement the other two, remained in limbo until the coming of the TVA, when it was finally built and named Wheeler Dam.

After the completion of Wilson Dam, the entire Muscle Shoals project went into a state of suspended animation. Auto magnate Henry Ford offered to buy the nitrate works and turn them into fertilizer plants, but Congress refused to accept the proposal. Other schemes for handing the nitrate works over to private industry also failed.

The chief opponent of private use of Muscle Shoals was Senator George W. Norris of Nebraska. His idea was to turn the nitrate works over to the U.S. Department of Agriculture for experimental uses, and to run the Wilson Dam power plant through a Federally owned corporation.

All during the Twenties, various Congressional committees debated the disposition of Muscle Shoals, with Republican Senator Norris battling against Republican Congressmen and Presidents to keep the Wilson Dam complex out of private hands. Meanwhile the nitrate plants were serving no purpose at all, nor was Wilson Dam providing a satisfactory power supply.

The problem with the Wilson Dam hydroelectric output lay in the nature of the river. In the dry summer months the Tennessee's flow diminished and greatly limited the efficiency of the hydroelectric plant. The Army Engineers' "Dam Number Three," upstream, would have retained spring flood waters in a reservoir and released them to the turbines in the dry months. But "Dam Number Three" remained unbuilt while Congress debated. Such power as the Wilson Dam did generate was sold by the Government to the Alabama Power Company, its one customer at the time.

While the tedious controversy over what to do with Muscle Shoals dragged on, the Tennessee River continued to behave as it always had. Disastrous floods had punished the Tennessee Valley in 1917, 1926, and 1927, making hundreds of thousands homeless and ruining a vast acreage of farmland. The economy of the region lagged hopelessly. Shipping was insignificant as a local industry. Farming was paralyzed by the floods. Farmers lived without electricity because there were no power plants.

Senator Norris sponsored bills for the Federal maintenance and development of the entire valley, but they were vetoed by Presidents Coolidge and Hoover. President Hoover said of one of them, "That is not liberalism, it is degeneration." The land was wasting away, and nothing was being done. An Army Engineers study recommending the construction of a series of dams on the Tennessee was pigeonholed in 1930, a year before Hoover's veto of the Norris development bill.

Then came 1933. Into office swept Franklin Delano Roosevelt, his mission being to revitalize depression-stunned America and to transform our underdeveloped regions into thriving centers of prosperity. In his campaign in 1932 he had recommended development of four major Government power projects, including Muscle Shoals and the St. Lawrence Seaway, which will be discussed later on. A month after he took office he sent a message to Congress:

"It is clear that the Muscle Shoals development is but a small part of the potential public usefulness of the entire Tennessee River." And he declared, "The continued idleness of a great national investment in the Tennessee Valley leads me to ask the Congress for legislation necessary to enlist this project in the service of the people."

Congress, in 1933, refused President Roosevelt nothing. Senator Norris, hailing the end of what he called a "twelve years' struggle waged on behalf of the common people against the combined forces of monopoly and greed," helped to frame the act that brought the TVA into being. The TVA would take over Muscle Shoals. It would see through to completion "Dam Number Three," Wheeler Dam. It would build what it needed to reinvigorate the entire Tennessee Valley. It was authorized to sell its surplus power to "states, counties, municipalities, corporations, partnerships, or individuals."

The purposes of the TVA, as set forth in the act, were:

"1. The maximum amount of flood control;

"2. The maximum development of said Tennessee River for navigation purposes;

"3. The maximum generation of electric power consistent with flood control and navigation;

"4. The proper use of marginal lands;

"5. The proper method of reforestation of all lands in said drainage basin suitable for reforestation; and

"6. The economic and social well-being of the people living in said river basin."

The people living in said river basin were badly in need of some attention to their economic and social well-being. In some counties 87 per cent of the families were receiving public welfare support. Actual starvation was not uncommon. Of the Valley's 26,000,000 acres, nearly one third were hurt by erosion. In Jefferson County, in east Tennessee, "35% of the land had lost more than one-half of its topsoil, 42.4% had lost two thirds or more of its topsoil, and 2.9% had substantially been destroyed." Floods had caused an average of $2,000,000 damage a year for more years than anyone wanted to remember. Only two farms in a hundred had electricity. Because of the region's poverty, there was no money to build decent homes, adequate schools, usable highways.

The discontented young people of the Valley were leaving for other parts of the country. Only the discouraged, the defeated, were staying behind. Decay and dismay were the prevailing symbols of life in the Tennessee Valley, while untapped power and fertile topsoil went rushing through the riverbed toward the Ohio.

The President appointed Dr. Arthur E. Morgan, President of Antioch College, as chairman of TVA. The other two members of the Authority were Dr. Harcourt A. Morgan, an agricultural specialist and President of the University of Tennessee, and David E. Lilienthal, a lawyer and member of the Wisconsin Public Service Commission.

The three directors held their first meeting on June 16, 1933. They set up headquarters in Knoxville, Tennessee, and, with the whole nation watching intently, they set about the job of taming the Tennessee.

DAMS AND MORE DAMS

Dams, dams, dams—that was the TVA's answer to the challenge. Norris Dam, named for the great Nebraska Senator who had spearheaded the TVA idea for a decade and more, was the first. Construction began on October 1, 1933, and was ended on July 28, 1936. Norris Dam is 265 feet high, 1,860 feet in length, and cost $31,500,000, and has a generating capacity of 100,800 kilowatts.

As at Hoover Dam, a town was built from scratch to house the Norris Dam workers. In a month's time, the plans for Norris, Tennessee, were drawn. The town was built 3 miles from the dam site and 25 miles from Knoxville. The town itself served as something of an experiment in town planning, with curved streets and walks, plenty of wooded acreage, and houses built back from the streets at angles chosen carefully to accent the sun, the breeze, and the view. The town was owned by the Government until 1948, but now is the property of its residents, and is one of the loveliest towns in Tennessee.

The Army Engineers had previously studied the dam site, at Cove Creek, Tennessee, on the Clinch River, one of the five main tributaries of the Tennessee. The TVA now took over these earlier plans for a Cove Creek Dam.

They decided on a gravity-type dam (that is, one in which the sheer weight of the concrete holds back the water) and set about testing and planning. Surveys of the reservoir area were begun, test drillings were made to see if the rock surrounding the dam site could stand the weight of the dam, earthquake surveys were conducted.

Then land was bought, thousands of acres of it. Every family that lived in the reservoir area had to be relocated. Power lines, telephone lines, railroad tracks, barns, even graveyards—all had to be moved back out of the reach of the water. Every tree in the reservoir area had to be cleared away; otherwise, drowned trees would be swept downstream in years to come, blocking navigation and endangering the dam.

Work began at the east bank of the Clinch River. Here, the land sloped away gently from the water, meaning that the dam would have to extend farther than on the west. The all-important first excavation was made at the place where the shoulder of the dam would fit into the rock abutment. The rubble carved from the hill was used to reinforce the coffer-dam to hold back the water.

A second cofferdam on the west side complemented the first. Between the two cofferdams, a narrow gap was left, and the river passed through, to be pumped away. Excavations be-gan in the dry part of the bed. The east and west banks were weathered, rotted, and full of caves, and had to be cemented to prevent leakage. Dynamite and steam shovels were used to carve the bedrock into the proper shape for the big dam, and finally the foundation was scrubbed clean to guarantee a tight fit when the concrete of the dam was poured.

A quarry on the west side of the dam served as the source of the stone for the dam. The quarriers worked in such a way as to create a natural boat harbor out of this hill, for the future use of the people of the area.

The stone drawn from the hill was pulverized, limestone sand was added, then cement and water. Wood forms pro-vided a framework for the dam, and soon the concrete was flowing and the dam was rising, everywhere but at the nar-row gap through which the river still ran.

When the incomplete dam rose above the height of the river, a third cofferdam was built, rising from the dry land inside the first two cofferdams. Although the first two coffer-dams had timber sides, the third was sided with concrete. When it was complete, the river was diverted through com-pleted portions of the dam, passing through slide gates, and work began to close the gap.

Concrete shrinks as it sets. The dam-builders provided for contraction joints every 56 feet. When the cooling blocks had set, these joints were filled with grout to make the dam water-tight.

Construction of the powerhouse, on the east side of the river, began as soon as the rock base at the powerhouse site had been covered with concrete. The conduits that would bring water through the dam to the turbines were shaped, with two steel-lined penstocks, 20 feet in diameter, placed on a 12-degree slope to carry water pouring downward onto the vanes of the turbines. Other tubes were placed to carry the water past the turbines and out the front of the dam into the river again.

The spillway parts of the dam—through which the main body of the water was to flow—were also constructed early, so that the spillway gates could be used to divert the river while the dam was in its last phases of construction. Only in times of very high water does the river actually pass over the crest of the spillway of a dam; more usually, the water is sluiced off through the spillway's gates, near the base of the dam.

The concrete at Norris—as at any dam where the abutments are high enough—was poured in a standard manner. Two towers were built at opposite ends of the dam, and between these towers, nearly 2,000 feet apart, steel cables of enormous strength were run. The towers themselves were movable, sliding on tracks inward or outward from the riverbed. Heavy materials—buckets of concrete, or sluice gates, or anything else needed in the construction of the dam—were carried by truck to the west tower, where great steel hooks seized them, swung them out over the abyss, and lowered them into place.

Finishing touches were put on the big dam early in 1936, and in May of that year the gates were closed, allowing the reservoir to begin backing up. Two months later, the generators were turning out power for Tennessee, and the first of the TVA dams—which are some 30 in number today—was complete. The reservoir, Norris Lake, was developed by TVA as a recreational area and state park, and more than 100,000 people a year enjoy the use of its facilities.

The TVA had taken over the old Wilson Dam, which had

been completed in 1925. To make Wilson Dam more efficient, "Dam Number Three" had to be built—and so, a month after Norris Dam was begun, TVA engineers were at work on Wheeler Dam, upstream from Wilson in the Muscle Shoals area.

Wheeler Dam is the lowest of TVA's main river dams, only 72 feet high. Its construction started on November 21, 1933, from plans previously developed by the Army Engineers and the Bureau of Reclamation. It stretches 6,342 feet across the river, generates a quarter of a million kilowatts, and cost $48,000,000 to build. Part of the dam is concrete, but near the navigation lock it is a combination of concrete and steel-truss piers.

A year and a half later, Wheeler Dam was joined by Pickwick Landing Dam, 52 miles downstream of Wilson Dam. This dam completed the job of deepening the water in the shoals region of the river's northern Alabama course, eliminating rapids, hidden rocks, and whirlpools. Pickwick Landing Dam is 113 feet high, 7,715 feet long, and cost $47,000,000; it was completed in 1938 and has a generating capacity of 216,000 kilowatts. As at many of the TVA dams, Pickwick Landing is also the site of a public recreation area, and a town has sprung up where the construction camp was located. Pickwick Dam is a combination type; its powerhouse, spillway, and lock sections are made of concrete and steel, while the rest of the dam, a mile long, is earth and rock.

Fourth of the TVA dams was Guntersville Dam, also in Alabama, begun in 1935 and completed in 1939. Like Pickwick Landing and many of the other main river dams, Guntersville Dam is an earth and rock dam, with only the powerhouse, spillway, and lock sections made of concrete and steel. If floodwaters ever reached the top of the earth embankment, the dam would be washed out in a matter of hours—but Guntersville's spillway system has been designed so that no imaginable flood could ever top the embankments. Guntersville's maximum height is 94 feet, its length 3,979 feet. It cost $39,000,000 to build, and generates 97,200 kilowatts of power.

Guntersville Dam has completely transformed the town of Guntersville. Some 30 years ago, Guntersville was an insignificant little river hamlet. It has grown into an important port since the widening and deepening of the river through the TVA, and the hundredfold increase in river commerce.

A month after work began at Guntersville—which is at the Tennessee's southernmost reach—construction started at Chickamauga Dam, farther upstream, just upriver from the city of Chattanooga, Tennessee. Chattanooga had suffered more than any city from floods along the Tennessee. Nineteen times between 1910 and 1930 the river had flooded there, with disastrous consequences three times and considerable damage in many years. Chickamauga Dam, 1 mile long and 129 feet high, was designed not only to generate power—108,000 kilowatts—but to protect the city of Chattanooga. A creek was diverted to empty into the river below instead of above the dam, and a reservoir to hold back the floodwaters was established.

The value of Chickamauga Dam to the city of Chattanooga was demonstrated in January 1957, when the swollen Tennessee reached a peak 24 feet above flood stage. But for the dam, the water would have flooded the city, causing damage that might have reached $75,000,000. Instead, the flood, second greatest in the city's history, did only slight damage.

The job of taming the Tennessee was just about complete with the building of Chickamauga, which was finished in March 1940. The main stretch of the Tennessee was under control and suitable for navigation, and power was being generated for the people and industries of the Valley. To write finis to the job in the proper way, the TVA bought, in 1939, the elderly, leaky Hales Bar Dam, built privately from 1905 to 1913, and remodeled and greatly expanded it to bring it in line with modern power and navigation needs.

These six dams—Chickamauga, Hales Bar, Guntersville, Wheeler, Wilson, and Pickwick Landing—transformed the Tennessee from Chattanooga down to northern Alabama by 1940. The heart of the river was under control. Now work began to extend man's sway all the way down the river from Knoxville to its meeting with the Ohio.

This new phase of the TVA's task got under way on July 11, 1939, with the construction of the Kentucky Dam, greatest of all the TVA dams. It is 8,422 feet long and 206 feet high; this monster cost $119,200,000 and created a reservoir 184 miles long, Kentucky Lake, whose maximum storage capacity is nearly twice that of Norris Lake, though only a fifth that of Lake Mead. Both a highway and a railroad pass across the top of Kentucky Dam.

Kentucky Dam is located near the mouth of the Tennessee, 20-odd miles above Paducah. It permits navigation from the Ohio River up the Tennessee for several hundred miles.

You may have been wondering how, if the river is blocked by a dam, boats can proceed at all. The job is handled by locks, which are actually elevators for lifting river-going vessels. We will deal in detail with locks when we reach the chapter about the St. Lawrence Seaway.

Because Kentucky Dam must handle large towboats coming off the Ohio River, its lock is of unusual size. The dam itself follows the pattern of Guntersville and others—steel and concrete for the lock, spillway, and power plant, earth and rock elsewhere. It took 7 million cubic yards of concrete, earth, and rock to build Kentucky Dam.

Two more dams remained to be built in order to make the Tennessee navigable from the Ohio River to Knoxville. The first of these, Watts Bar Dam, got under way the same month as Kentucky Dam, July 1939, and was finished in February 1942. Watts Bar Dam, located midway between Chattanooga and Knoxville, was originally designed to have only three active generators. But as the gathering stormclouds of World War II became more threatening, it was decided to use five generators instead. A crash construction program got Watts Bar into operation only a few months after the war had started, supplying badly needed power for the war effort.

Last of the actual Tennessee River dams is Fort Loudoun Dam, begun in July 1940, and completed 3½ years later at a cost of $43,000,000. For many years this dam, just below Knoxville, boasted the highest single lift, 80 feet, of any navigation lock in the world. This figure has now been surpassed, but the lock itself remains an impressive achievement for its day. Fort Loudoun Dam, 4,190 feet long and 122 feet high, is one of the most graceful and handsome of all the many TVA dams. By the time it was designed, TVA's engineers had attained the most minute familiarity with the special problems of building dams on the Tennessee, and in this one they were able to blend usefulness and attractiveness to the highest degree. For this reason, Fort Loudoun Dam, near Lenoir City, Tennessee, is extremely popular with tourists, and guided tours are available.

With the completion of Fort Loudoun, the job of building the main-river dams was done. From Knoxville to Paducah they ran, 9 dams in all, 7 of them built entirely by the TVA. The 9 dams converted the Tennessee Valley into a land of lakes, big lakes, whose total area is more than half that of the State of Rhode Island. The river was now open to heavy shipping. The people of the Valley had a limitless supply of electric power, sold to them at nonprofit rates by the TVA. Chattanooga and the other flood-wracked cities and towns could relax for the first time in high-water months.

But there was plenty yet to do. The dams on the tributaries of the Tennessee had to be built next, to allow complete control of the river back of its source.

These dams were of a different type. The main-river dams were long and low, with concrete spillways and locks, earth and rock-fill elsewhere. The tributary dams had to be higher and narrower. They were built of concrete. They did not need locks, for there was no shipping on the tributaries.

First of the tributary dams was also the first of all the TVA dams: Norris Dam, on the Clinch. After Norris, attention turned to the main-river dams, and so the next tributary dam was not begun for 4 years. It was Hiwassee Dam, begun in July 1937 and finished in May 1940.

Like most of the tributary dams, Hiwassee's chief purpose

was not power generation but flood storage. During the winter its reservoir is low, but the water level builds all through the spring, and then the impounded water is released to feed into the Tennessee River during the dry summer months. Hiwassee is located in North Carolina, in a region that receives more rainfall than any part of the country except the Pacific Northwest. The dam is 1,376 feet in length, 307 feet high—dimensions strikingly different from those of the main-river dams. At first Hiwassee had only one generator, but a second was installed in 1956. This new generator is unusual in that it is equipped with a turbine that reverses, so that water can be pumped back into the reservoir for storage in times of low power demand, to be used when power needs are high.

Next of the tributary dams was Cherokee, on which construction started on August 1, 1940. Europe was at war by that time, and it seemed inevitable that the United States would be drawn into the conflict. Power was needed, power to build guns and tanks and planes. The War Department asked the TVA to do its best to increase the generating capacity of the Tennessee Valley, since a power shortage was predicted if we got into the war.

TVA responded by building a new dam on the Holston River, 40 miles above Knoxville. It gave itself a deadline of just 21 months to build the dam and get it into production. To meet this deadline, the designers adopted features from other TVA dams, combining them into a new dam to fit the needs of the Holston River Site. The result was Cherokee Dam, at 6,760 feet the longest of the tributary dams. The 175-foot-high dam was built in 16 months, a world's record. The gates were closed 2 days before Pearl Harbor, and the reservoir began to back up. By April 1942—the 21st month, and 2 weeks ahead of schedule—power from Cherokee Dam was flowing into war plants.

The Cherokee Dam construction record did not last long. Power and more power was needed, now that we were at war. Another tributary project, on the French Broad River, was authorized in January 1942. Congress had refused to provide an appropriation for this project in 1941, but the changed circumstances of wartime made the lawmakers reverse their decision. Construction began on Douglas Dam on February 2, 1942. On March 21, 1943—13½ months later—the job was done. No major concrete dam had ever been built with such breathless speed before, and the record may last a long time.

Time was saved on Douglas Dam because it was almost a twin of Cherokee, 20 miles away. The same blueprints were used, with only minor modifications, and the construction equipment and labor crews were moved from Cherokee to Douglas as the job proceeded at both sites.

While this backbreaking double job was being rushed to completion in upper Tennessee, four other tributary dams were rising in the Hiwassee River Basin of North Carolina, lower Tennessee, and Georgia. These four dams—the Apalachia, Chatuge, Ocoee No. 3, and Nottely—were designed to fit in with four existing dams in the basin. Three of these four —Ocoee Nos. 1 and 2, and Blue Ridge—had been built prior to TVA and were acquired from the Tennessee Electric Power Company. The fourth was TVA-built Hiwassee Dam.

Construction began on all four new dams the same day —July 17, 1941. The Apalachia Dam, completed in September 1943, was placed 10 miles downstream from Hiwassee Dam, but its powerhouse is 8 miles farther along. This odd separation gets maximum value out of a rapid drop in the riverbed. A steel tube 18 feet in diameter carries the water through the mountains to the powerhouse, where it generates electricity with far greater force than otherwise.

Chatuge, completed in just 7 months, is the only TVA dam constructed entirely without concrete. This simple dam, 2,850 feet long and 144 feet high, is made of tightly packed earth, faced on its upstream side with a layer of small stones, or what dam-builders call "rip-rap." Such dams are considerably cheaper to build than concrete dams, but are also far less versatile and are not suited for many sites. A powerhouse was added to the original Chatuge Dam in 1954, capable of generating 10,000 kilowatts.

Third of the Hiwassee Basin Dams of 1941 was Ocoee No. 3, completed in April 1943. As at Apalachia, it was found that the best site for the dam was not also the best site for a powerhouse, and so Ocoee No. 3's powerhouse is 2½ miles farther downstream. Ocoee No. 3 is a "ghost" dam. Its powerhouse and its spillways are operated by remote control, from the old Ocoee No. 2 Dam upstream, and so Ocoee No. 3 has no permanent staff and no facilities for visitors.

Last of the 1941 quartet was Nottely Dam, finished in a mere 6 months. Like Chatuge, Nottely is a simple rolled-earth dam, but is strengthened by the addition of heavy shoulders of rock. The powerhouse, added in 1955, generates 15,000 kilowatts.

The most spectacular of the TVA dams, Fontana Dam, was the next to be begun. It got under way on January 1, 1942, less than a month after the Pearl Harbor attack that brought this country into the Second World War. Thus, the TVA was faced with a brand-new construction problem: wartime shortages. Many of the most skilled construction men were on their way to war, and as the job proceeded it became harder and harder to obtain replacements. Materials, too, were hard to get. Priorities went to other urgent demands.

It took 3 years to build Fontana Dam. At 480 feet, it is the highest dam in the United States east of the Rockies. Its great mass—it is 2,365 feet in length—is made to seem even greater by its design, which is level and sweeping and simple. Six thousand workmen labored on Fontana, forcing the river into diversion tunnels while the concrete was being poured. Today, only a handful of men are needed to maintain the power plant, and the construction camp has been turned into a popular resort on the Little Tennessee River for the public to enjoy.

A month after Fontana was started, work began on a dam on the South Fork of the Holston River, in northeastern Tennessee near the Virginia border. War shortages, however, forced the suspension of work in 1943. The workmen returned to build the South Holston Dam in August 1947, finishing the job early in 1951. South Holston is a rolled-earth-and-rock dam, similar to the Nottely Dam in the Hiwassee Basin.

Not far to the south of South Holston Dam, another dam had also been begun in 1942 and then discontinued. Work resumed on the Watauga Dam in the summer of 1946, lasting three years. Watauga Dam was designed in three sections: the dam itself, a 900-foot-long barrier of earth and rock; the powerhouse, a mile below the dam; and the visitors' center, a few hundred yards above the dam, where the work of the TVA is explained daily.

During the Fifties, TVA continued to expand its network of tributary dams. 1950 saw the start of Boone Dam and the remodeling of the pre-TVA Wilbur Dam; 1951 marked the beginning of work on the Fort Patrick Henry Dam, TVA's twentieth in twenty years; others have followed, and the job is not yet complete.

The latest of the TVA's dams is the $34,000,000 Melton Hill Dam, on the Clinch River, not far from Norris Dam. Melton Dam is 19 miles west of Knoxville and 9 miles southwest of the city of Oak Ridge, where experimental atomic energy research demands a good deal of power. The Melton Hill Dam, going into operation in the summer of 1963, has an initial capacity of 72,000 kilowatts.

The dam is unusual among the TVA dams in that its power plant was not financed by Congressional appropriations. In 1960 Congress gave the TVA the right to sell bonds to the public to finance its power capacity. Until that year all TVA construction was paid for by direct Government grant.

In recent years, however, the TVA administrators have slackened the dam-building pace, preferring to construct steam plants for the generation of power. The current TVA administrators feel that steam plants provide a quicker way of increasing the Valley's power capacity, and that, with most of the flood problem under control, steam plants were higher on the priority list than dams in the more remote tributary regions.

Steam plants produce power from coal. A conveyer carries

crushed coal from pulverizers to a boiler, where it is used to heat water, producing steam that drives turbines. The postwar steam plants vastly expanded TVA's power capacity.

TVA is more than just dams and steam plants, of course. Valley development has involved the building of bridges and roads, of public recreation areas, and other nonpower projects. But the heart of the TVA is its dam system, the most extensive in the world.

The change that the TVA and its dams have brought to the Tennessee Valley since 1933 is awesome. The river is navigable for 650 miles, all the year round. Farms have spread greenly over one-time eroded wasteland. Families that had never seen an electric light before 1933 now have washing machines, television sets, refrigerators.

The benefits of TVA reach far beyond the Tennessee Valley. Three times in recent years, the TVA has literally "turned off" the Tennessee, shutting all gates and keeping back the water to ease the problems of the flood-stricken Ohio and Missisippi Valleys. Industry has thrived in the Valley, with economic benefits for the entire nation.

The Tennessee is the most completely controlled river in the world. From time to time it shifts restlessly, trying to throw off its shackles, but the dams will have none of that. They keep the Tennessee securely pinioned.

The story of the TVA and its dams is a giant one, and it has only been possible to sketch it briefly here. No one, however, can read even a few pages about the TVA without feeling a sense of the greatness of the accomplishment. Nor can anyone—even the conservatives who to this day denounce the TVA as "socialistic" and "authoritarian," and demand its sale to private interests—fail to recognize the imposing magnitude of this series of dams, and to feel a surge of pride at the awareness that so puny an animal as man can tame so mighty a thing as a river.

7

Grand Coulee Dam

~~~~~~
~~~~~~

THERE are many kinds of "biggest" dam. At this writing, the Vaiont Dam in Italy is the highest in the world. The Fort Peck Dam, in Missouri, is the greatest in length, and also in volume. Hoover Dam has the biggest reservoir, though not for long. (When the Kariba Dam's reservoir in Africa is full, it will surpass Lake Mead fourfold.)

Grand Coulee Dam, which the American Society of Civil Engineers named, along with Hoover Dam, as one of the Seven Modern Civil Engineering Wonders of the United States, holds one title that it is likely to keep for some time to come. It is the most massive concrete structure in the world. More than 10 million cubic yards of concrete were needed to do the job for which Grand Coulee was planned: damming the Columbia River. No other concrete dam even comes close in sheer volume.

Like the TVA, Grand Coulee Dam was a New Deal project, though it had been first discussed when Theodore, not Franklin, Roosevelt was in the White House. The Columbia River, which rises in the Canadian Rockies and plunges at a head-long clip through the states of Washington and Oregon toward the Pacific, is one of the most powerful of all rivers. On this continent, only the Mississippi, the Mackenzie, and the St. Lawrence surpass it in volume of flow—and the Columbia is far more vigorous than any of those. "The Mother of Rivers," it has been called. It has many sources, many tributaries. Its drainage basin covers 259,000 square miles (including 39,700 square miles in Canada). The Columbia's basin contains some 7 per cent of the total area of continental United States excluding Alaska—and 40 per cent of the country's potential hydroelectric power.

Until the building of Grand Coulee, this vast potential of power was sweeping uselessly out to sea, while the people of Washington and Oregon watched longingly but helplessly. The Pacific Northwest languished, without enough power for industry, without enough water for its farms, and the key to prosperity lay glittering out of reach in the Columbia River.

Small wonder, then, that the people of the Northwest dreamed of a dam on the Columbia, to intercept its rushing waters and tap off a power and irrigation supply. Back in 1904, the U.S. Reclamation Service studied the drought-ridden, sparsely populated area, but nothing was done.

Fourteen years later, the first seeds of the Grand Coulee idea were planted. Thousands of years ago, the bed of the Columbia had been displaced by a glacier. A natural dam of ice had forced the river to cut a new channel for itself—the Grand Coulee, or Big Spill. When the glaciers retreated, the river returned to its original channel—leaving Grand Coulee, a dry gorge of great size.

There stood this great chasm, this dry gulch slashing through the lava fields of central Washington. "Why not seal it off at both ends," the people of the Northwest asked, "and turn it into an irrigation reservoir?"

There was an engineering problem of no little size involved, though. The ancient chasm was hundreds of feet above the present-day level of the Columbia. How could the water ever be pumped high enough to reach the Grand Coulee gorge? Impossible! And how could anyone build a dam big enough to lift the water to that height without also flooding half of Canada?

The Grand Coulee idea seemed to founder right there. No one could see how a dam of the proper size could be built, nor were there pumps to handle the job of lifting the water to the reservoir. And the dam, if it were built at all, would have to be multi-purpose, providing power as well as irrigation, or it would not pay its way.

A newspaperman named Rufus Woods carried on a campaign for years to interest the planners in the project. A group calling itself the Columbia Basin Irrigation League was formed to promote the idea of a Grand Coulee Dam. By 1932 the Bureau of Reclamation had drafted plans for a workable dam on the site—a combination dam and pumping station that would lift the water the necessary hundreds of feet, into the Grand Coulee gorge, where it could be used for power and irrigation. But President Hoover refused to request a Congressional appropriation for the project, and it got nowhere.

The following year the idea was revived by the new Roosevelt Administration, with its keen interest in public power. The new President authorized the expenditure of $60,000,000 for the job—though it would cost far more before it was completed, and would be an enormously more ambitious project than anyone had envisioned in 1933.

As usual, the scheme was denounced by those who did not stand to benefit directly from it. Francis G. Culkin, a Republican Congressman from New York, described Grand Coulee as "a vast area of gloomy tablelands interspersed with deep gullies," and insisted that there was no one in the region "to sell power to except rattlesnakes, coyotes, and rabbits. Everyone knows that. There is no market for power in the Northwest . . . absolutely no market for the power in this section and will not be for many years to come."

The people of the Columbia Basin, though, begged to differ with the gentleman from New York. They welcomed the

Grand Coulee project with glee, for they saw that the salvation of their region was at hand.

Probably no one realized the full scope of the job at the beginning. A year or two of preliminary studies told the tale, however. And when construction began, in December 1935, it was with the realization that when it was complete it would be the largest man-made structure in the history of the world.

The job was twofold. First, a dam had to be built across the Columbia to form a reservoir and to provide a source of hydroelectric power. Then, the Grand Coulee gorge had to be sealed off, and water pumped from the lower reservoir to the higher one, and thence to the surrounding farmland.

First, the dam. Three towns were created to house the workers, since the dam site, midway down the 1,214-mile course of the Columbia, was in a desolate, empty region of the State of Washington. In Coulee City, the supervising engineers were to live; in Mason City, the foremen; in Grand Coulee, the ordinary laborers. Once these towns had been built, work could begin on the massive job of laying bare the riverbed for the foundations of the dam.

Work started on the western bank. A semicircular line of steel cofferdams, 3,000 feet long, was constructed, stretching from the bank out into the river and then back to the bank again. Each cofferdam in this line was filled with earth and rubble as blasting proceeded in the riverbed. Steam shovels scooped out enormous bites of the bed, cutting down toward the solid rock beneath.

When work was finished at the western end of the dam site, the crews moved on into midstream. Here, more massive cofferdams were erected around a 50-acre space that was then pumped free of water, and the excavating and concrete-pouring began there.

During this stage of the construction work, part of the cofferdam system gave way under the steady pressure of the current. Some 40,000 gallons of water a minute began to pour into the construction area.

Every man available was ordered to drop all other work

and rush to the breakthrough site. Day and night, in 2-hour shifts, the men fought the river back. Ten-ton concrete buckets suspended from the trestle bridge along the canyon wall carried them down into the work area. As pumps strained to spurt out the inrushing water, the workmen struggled to plug the gap. Hundreds of tons of fill went into the break, but still the river came through. Finally a substance called Dentonite, which swells to fifteen times its ordinary size when wet, was poured into the break by the ton. As it swelled, the waters were forced back. The break cost several lives, and half a million dollars in lost time.

Later, a landslide threatened the construction. A million cubic yards of earth and rock on the west bank began to slide down into the excavation. Workmen hastily blocked the slide with a barrage of rock. Engineers examined the site and discovered that the slide material was resting on a bed of watery clay. The clay provided a slick path on which the landslide could move with ease. Tunnels hundreds of feet long were driven through the clay to drain off the water and reduce the slipperiness.

A third catastrophe loomed soon afterward on the opposite bank: another landslide. A mass of material was descending at a rate of 2 feet an hour. At first, the puzzled engineers could find no way of stopping it. In desperation, they decided to freeze the slide. Workmen drove 6 miles of piping into the ground, and ice-cold brine was forced in. The brine froze the slide and halted its advance.

The work continued. Concrete-mixing plants on either side of the river turned out endless thousands of tons of concrete, which were carried by a traveling chain of buckets to the 50-ton crane that lowered them into the excavation. The great dam was honeycombed with thousands of pipes to speed up the cooling process. As mentioned before, concrete shrinks as it hardens, and gives off great heat. The engineers estimated that it would have taken 150 years for the concrete of the dam to cool naturally. But icy water, passing through the concealed pipes, reduced each section of concrete to normal temperature in a month, allowing construction to continue smoothly and evenly without halts for cooling. There were 2,000 miles of pipes used in this fashion.

By 1940 most of the job was done, and water began to rise in the lake back of the dam. On March 22, 1941, the first power was drawn from two small service generators at the dam. In August, a 150,000-horsepower turbine began to turn. And by 1942 the big dam was in full operation as a source of hydroelectric power. The water of its lake—named Roosevelt Lake—began to back up toward the Canadian border, ultimately reaching a length of more than 150 miles.

The dam is a giant even among giants. Across its front, the Great Pyramid of Egypt could be flanked by a foursome of U.S. Capitol Buildings with some room left over. Four huge ocean liners the size of the *Queen Elizabeth* and the *Queen Mary* could moor side by side at the dam, so wide is it. Over its wall at high water comes a cascade more than twice the height of Niagara Falls.

And from this 10-million-cubic-yard slab of concrete and steel came power. Penstock linings 18 feet in diameter, wide enough for an express train, were installed to carry water to the turbines—eighteen giant pipes, carrying enough water to supply every person on earth with a gallon an hour.

"There is no market for power in the Northwest," Representative Culkin had said a decade before Grand Coulee was finished. Even while the dam was going up, many people had the same idea. "Who's going to buy all this power? Why so much capacity? Who needs it?"

The aluminum industry needed it, for one. As the dam took shape, aluminum factories were rapidly built in the Northwest. It takes power to make aluminum, great quantities of power. Bauxite—aluminum ore—is mined in states like Arkansas, Alabama, and Louisiana, and refined into the white powder called alumina. Then the alumina is shipped to the aluminum factories of the Northwest, made possible by cheap power from the Columbia. There, an intricate process reduces the powder to metallic aluminum. The essential part of the process involves passing an electric current through an alumina solution. The molten metal cools, and is cast into pigs and then into ingots.

It takes 4 to 6 pounds of bauxite to make 2 pounds of alumina. Those 2 pounds of alumina yield 1 pound of aluminum. To make that pound of aluminum, 10 kilowatt-hours of electricity are required. (A kilowatt, or 1,000 watts, is the common standard of electrical measurement. A kilowatt-hour is a thousand watts of energy used for an hour. A kilowatt-hour is enough energy to run a washing machine 3 or 4 hours.)

Before the advent of cheap electrical power, aluminum was as expensive as gold. In 1884, the Washington Monument was tipped with an aluminum block weighing an even hundred ounces—the largest single block of aluminum ever cast up till that time. Today, Grand Coulee Dam's generators, if they were used exclusively for the production of power for aluminum factories, could aid in the casting of *ten* solid aluminum Washington Monuments, 555 feet tall, every year—with power to spare. Not surprising, then, that the State of Washington, drawing on Grand Coulee power, produces more aluminum than any other state.

Another industry that did not exist in the Northwest when Representative Culkin made his gloomy prediction was the atomic energy industry. It wasn't even dreamed of, back in 1933. But to Hanford, Washington, came a secret atomics plant in 1943. At Hanford a plant sprang up overnight, for the purpose of turning nonfissionable Uranium 238 into fissionable Plutonium 239, needed for atomic bombs.

Manufacturing plutonium from uranium takes power too —even more than aluminum-manufacturing. In the atomic reactor, steady neutron bombardment gradually transforms the harmless uranium into the deadly plutonium, a process accompanied by enormous heat. Giant pumps are needed to pour millions of gallons of water through the tubes of the reactor, carrying off the heat. The eight production reactors at the no-longer-secret Hanford plant use as much electricity a year as

Washington, D.C. Someday, atomic reactors themselves will be providing power aplenty. But until that time, the Hanford plant must draw its power from the generators at Grand Coulee Dam.

The tremendous expansion of the aluminum industry, and the needs of the atomic energy plants, easily absorbed all the power that Grand Coulee had to offer. More dams were needed, it soon became apparent. Now nobody asked, "Who's going to buy all that power?" People asked, "When's the next dam going to be ready?"

The Columbia River's power potential was so great that even Grand Coulee did not begin to tap it. The river, in its rush from source to sea, drops 2,650 feet, the height of 16 Niagaras. This tremendous downward flow builds up vast potential power—equal to 2 million tank cars of fuel oil a year.

That power had to be tapped for the growing Northwest. Grand Coulee had to be supplemented.

The Bonneville Dam, in western Oregon, helped. This early New Deal project, completed years before Grand Coulee, dammed up the Cascade Rapids, a 5-mile stretch of wildly plunging water that had been an obstacle to navigation on the Columbia for decades. Bonneville Dam also produced hydroelectric power, which, as mentioned earlier, was sold cheaply to the public through the Bonneville Power Administration. Bonneville Dam produced 500,000 kilowatts of power, Grand Coulee four times as much. Together, they produced enough power to supply the cities of New York, Chicago, Philadelphia, Detroit, Los Angeles, and Cleveland. But this was still not enough for the booming Northwest and its heavy industries.

Other major dams followed in the Columbia Basin—Rock Island, Anderson Ranch, The Dalles, Chief Joseph, McNary, Hungry Horse, and a dozen more. The power grid began to grow to meet the new needs.

The Hungry Horse Dam was one of the biggest. Its crest is 2,100 feet long, and its height—564 feet—is 14 feet greater than that of Grand Coulee. Hungry Horse Dam, built of 2,900,000 cubic yards of concrete, is situated on the Flathead

River, a tributary of the Columbia, in Montana. A dense forest had to be cleared away before the reservoir, extending 35 miles upstream and covering 24,000 acres, could be allowed to fill. Work on constructing the dam itself could be carried on only from March to November each year, because of the fierce winter weather, but the dam was still finished ahead of schedule.

Another big tributary dam in the Columbia system is Swift Dam on the Lewis River, in the Cascade Mountains of Washington. This privately built dam, operated by the Pacific Power and Light Company, is of the earth-fill type, and is one of the highest earth dams in the world, rising 512 feet. Completed in 1959, it held its title only about a year before it was topped by the 538-foot Trinity Dam in California.

A grand total of 750,000 truckloads of pounded-down earth, totaling 15,300,000 cubic yards of material, went into the making of the Swift Dam. A million cubic yards of this was taken out of the streambed itself, after a tunnel almost 3,000 feet long had been built to divert the Lewis River. The Swift Dam's electrical generating capacity is hefty, 600,000,000 kilowatt hours of energy a year. It is a single-purpose dam, having no irrigation, flood control, or navigation functions.

The expanding power-production system of the Columbia Basin is reaching now into another tributary, the Snake River, between Oregon and Idaho. A host of projects are under consideration here, and many dams have already been built. But Snake River power plans have fallen afoul of the old controversy of private versus public power development, and the conflict has held back the construction timetable.

Because the power potential of the Columbia Basin is so great, and the arguments over who is to build what are so numerous and bitter, it has frequently been suggested that the Government create a Columbia Valley Authority to coordinate all the various and multitudinous power projects of the region. But there is no sign that the Government plans to take such a step.

The closest thing to unified activity in the Columbia Basin

is the Northwest Power Pool. This is a system linking the many Federal, local, and private power-generating dams, almost 200 of them, into a unified and co-operating grid. The area covered by the pool includes not only Washington and Oregon, but reaches eastward to Idaho and western Montana, and across the Canadian border into British Columbia.

The Power Pool insures continuous power in all regions. Since there are not yet enough high storage dams to hold the spring and summer flow on the Columbia and store it to generate power in dry months, power potential drops in some parts of the Columbia Basin. When there is high water in one area, there may be low water elsewhere. When one dam shuts down to fill its reservoirs, power is pumped in from other dams to keep service flowing. In 1953, when a flood put Grand Coulee's powerhouse out of commission for a while, other power dams in the pool carried the power load in the pinch. Trouble in British Columbia may be met with power from a thousand miles away in Oregon, or vice versa. In the absence of a CVA, the Northwest Power Pool brings a certain measure of co-ordination to what otherwise could be a highly chaotic situation.

GRAND COULEE DAM AND IRRIGATION

Our discussion of the power aspect of Grand Coulee Dam has led us into a general look at the power-production features of the entire Columbia Basin. Now let us return to Grand Coulee, and see how the second stage of the two-step power-and-irrigation project was completed.

It was not until 10 years after the completion of Grand Coulee Dam that its impounded water began to be used for irrigation. The first Grand Coulee water began to flow into the fields near Moses Lake, Washington, on May 29, 1952. The Commissioner of the Bureau of Reclamation turned on the tap, and sprinklers began to shower water down on the parched, dusty cropland of a 30-year-old soldier-turned-farmer named Donald D. Dunn.

The water was coming from the sealed reservoir that a

decade earlier had been the dry Grand Coulee gorge. Powerful pumps had lifted the water from Roosevelt Lake into the new reservoir, and from there, gravity canals and siphons carried it to 1,029,000 acres of thirsty farmland. At a rate of some 60,000 acres a year, the irrigation scheme was extended gradually over a vast stretch of the Northwest. Towns of Central Washington like Moses Lake, Ephrata, Quincy, and Othello are today just beginning to savor the real benefits of the giant dam that President Roosevelt authorized some 30 years before. Thriving fields of sugar beets, corn, beans, and potatoes, oceans of golden wheat, testify to the transformation wrought by Grand Coulee Dam.

The job of turning sagebrush land into beet-growing land had to be a slow one. First, the dam had to be built, a job that took until 1942. Then, Roosevelt Lake had to be allowed to back up to the Canadian border.

The old gorge was sealed by dams. The lower end of the gorge is blocked by a rock and earth-fill structure known as Dry Falls Dam. Beyond it is the cliff known as Dry Falls, once the site of a thundering 417-foot waterfall in prehistoric times when the gorge was the bed of the Columbia River.

Below the gorge is the awesome majesty of Grand Coulee Dam itself, 22 million tons of concrete, 550 feet high and more than 4,000 feet long at the crest. Miles of inspection galleries and shafts wind within the body of the dam. Two great powerhouses flank the spillway, which is twice as high, half as wide as Niagara Falls. A pumping plant is located at the west end of the dam, across from the powerhouses that feed power by long-distance transmission lines to the Bonneville Power Administration.

The pumps, operated by a 65,000-horsepower motor, take water from 80 feet below the surface of Roosevelt Lake, and, without seeming to strain at all, lift it 280 feet to a feeder canal that shoots it into the sealed reservoir of the gorge.

Filling that reservoir was carried out with deliberate slowness. For one thing, Grand Coulee Dam was being called on to deliver peak loads of power for much of the time, and there was little water to spare for irrigation. For another, the dam authorities did not want to fill the reservoir too fast. The gorge had been dry for many thousands of years, ever since the melting of the glaciers. The dam administrators wanted to give the gorge floor time to become thoroughly soaked again, before pouring in great quantities of water.

But soon the pumps were working steadily, and the 27-mile-long sealed reservoir started to fill. Steamboat Rock, which once had jutted up from the cliff, was fast becoming an island. Each pump, when operating at full power, was lifting a billion gallons of water a day—more water than is needed by the entire city of Chicago.

The surrounding farmland welcomes the water eagerly. And so Grand Coulee Dam serves its second function, that of bringing water to the fields. A great network of canals, totaling some 500 miles in length, serves to carry water out of the high-ground reservoir and to the farms.

8

A River Becomes a Seaway

~~~~~~

THE five Great Lakes—Superior, Michigan, Huron, Erie, and Ontario—together comprise the greatest body of fresh water on the earth. Lake Superior, the northernmost and western-most of the five, is the colossus of the group. Her waters flow into Lake Huron and Lake Michigan, and from there to Lake Erie. The 36-mile-long Niagara River drains the four Great Lakes into the fifth, Lake Ontario, forming incidentally on the way one of the great natural spectacles of the world, Niagara Falls.

The water continues eastward out of Lake Ontario via the St. Lawrence River, which hugs the boundary between the United States and Canada until it empties into the Atlantic. Until recent times, the St. Lawrence was an uneven river. Much of its 400-mile flow from Lake Ontario to Quebec was broad and deep, making it suitable for big ships. But in three places the river narrowed, and savage rocks in the shallow bed jutted upward to rip the belly out of any ship so foolish as to venture past. Thus the swift-flowing river was unsatisfactory for big cargo vessels. When a freighter of goodly size came in from Europe, bound with cargo for the ports of the Great Lakes, it had to stop at Montreal and go through the costly and time-consuming business of unloading and transferring its cargo to a flat-bottomed canalboat that would be able to navigate the rapids.

"Wouldn't it be wonderful," people said, "if we could deepen those rapids?" If the dangerous stretches of the St. Lawrence were somehow eliminated, the seaports of the world would have easy access to big inland cities like Chicago, Detroit, Milwaukee, and Duluth. And vice versa, too: the produce of those important industrial centers could be shipped easily and cheaply via seagoing vessels of large size.

Man has done plenty of tinkering with the Great Lakes and the St. Lawrence in the past. As early as 1700, a canal had been dug to bypass one of the St. Lawrence rapids. It was a small canal, not good for much besides barges, but it was a start at the job of coping with the problems of the region. Other small canals followed in the 18th century.

One big step toward creating an inland waterway came in the 1820's with the building of the Welland Canal. This canal sidestepped the biggest single obstacle between Lake Superior and the Atlantic on the waterway. Lake Erie is more than 300 feet higher than Lake Ontario. It might be possible to send shipping down the 326-foot grade of the Niagara River from Erie to Ontario but for one thing: half the drop is made in one fell swoop, at Niagara Falls. Not even in today's world of everyday miracles do we know how to navigate down waterfalls, let alone *up* them.

But we can go *around* them. Farseeing Canadian businessmen promoted the digging of a bypass canal 28 miles long, from Lakes Erie to Ontario. It would tap the water of the Welland River, a tributary of the Niagara. With great difficulty, the canal was built by 1830.

Of course, there was still the matter of that 326-foot drop in grade over the 30-some miles between the two lakes. But at least there was no Niagara Falls on the canal. Ships could be eased up and down the steep grade through a series of locks.

Locks are a very special type of dam used as "elevators" or "stairways" for river-going vessels. To put it as simply as possible, a lock is a man-made structure built right into the river, with walls on either side and a gate at each end. A ship that wants to navigate a steep upward slope enters the lock at the downstream end, and the gate is closed behind it. Then the sluices of the upstream gate are opened. Water flows into the lock, filling it just as a reservoir fills when a river is dammed. The ship floats upward until it is on the same level with the water beyond. Then the upstream gate opens and the ship passes through.

Locks are constructed in series where a grade is steep. Each lock may lift a ship 30 or 40 feet, so that it can continue on to the next lock in the series. On a busy day, there may be ships waiting in each lock of the series, moving on one at a time as the lock fills.

Going downstream is done the opposite way. A ship enters a full lock from the upstream side, and is gently lowered as the water runs out of the lock through the downstream sluice gates.

The first Welland Canal had many drawbacks. But it did the job for which it was designed. It enabled ships to go from Lake Erie to Lake Ontario for the first time. By 1832, clear-sighted men like John Young of Montreal were forecasting an era when there would be a seaway linking all five Great Lakes with the Atlantic Ocean.

Man continued to tinker with the waterway. Other small canals were built in the decades after the Welland. The next big job that had to be tackled was at Sault Ste. Marie, the outlet from Lake Superior to Lake Huron. A mile of deadly rapids boiled here, forming an impassable block from one big lake to the other. Eastward-bound wheat from the prairies and ore from the Michigan ranges had to travel overland by portage. Goods needed by the pioneers had to come westward the same way. Getting raw iron ore to the refineries of the East overland was a slow, expensive operation. The prosperity of Michigan depended on eliminating that mile of rapids at Sault Ste. Marie.

A man named Charles T. Harvey, whose job it was to sell weighing machines, found his imagination stirred by the idea of building a canal there. He raised the money, overcame political objections to the project, and built stone-lined locks of unthinkable size—350 feet long.

"You're out of your mind," people told him. "There'll never be a ship on the Great Lakes big enough to need a lock that size!"

Harvey only smiled and went on building his canal. He fought off mosquitoes in the summer, frostbite in the winter, and dug a mile-long ditch against formidable engineering problems. When he hit solid rock, he found he had to blast, but the nearest supply of dynamite was in Delaware, and the nearest city he could send a wire from was Detroit. That delayed the completion. The original survey had led him to think that he had to punch through a sand bar, not solid rock. He improvised a steam gravity punch that smashed half the rock by the time the dynamite could reach him.

By April 1855 the locks were finished and the gates were in place. All that remained to do was to make the final cut, at the west end of the canal, and let the waters of Lake Superior into the dry canal. But a cofferdam had to be erected to hold the water back until the cut was entirely finished. Harvey's engineer, Captain Canfield, died suddenly when the cofferdam was half finished. The incomplete dam would not hold, and there was no time to find another engineer.

Harvey's Yankee ingenuity did not fail him. He sent a man out to buy sailcloth, and unrolled a long bolt of it, filling it with gravel. The weighted sailcloth was laid across the mouth of the rapids—and it held. Digging could go on. The cut was finished, and water was sent into the canal. The job had taken 22½ months. On June 28, 1855, the S.S. *Illinois* became the first ship to pass from Lake Huron to Lake Superior. The overland portage had taken 20 days; the *Illinois* journeyed up the canal in 20 *minutes*. Another big step had been taken toward linking the Great Lakes with the Atlantic.

During the 1860's more canal-building along the St. Lawrence allowed some small ships to make the complete voyage from the Lakes to the ocean without unloading. But major work had to wait while the United States and Canada, which shared the use of the waterway, worked out treaties of co-operation.

Improvements in the waterway were constant. In 1876 a second lock was started at Sault Ste. Marie, the Weitzel Lock, which at 515 feet dwarfed Harvey's "unthinkable" 350-footer. But already ships big enough to crowd the Weitzel Lock were coming through, as sailing vessels gave way to steamships of imposing size and deep draft.

In 1892 the first shipload of iron ore from the Mesabi range came down from Lake Superior. There was an immediate foreign demand for this high-quality ore. But how could an ore boat make its way through the treacherous rapids of the St. Lawrence to the waiting ports of Europe?

More and more lock-building went on, chiefly at Sault Ste. Marie. In 1895 Canada built a new lock 900 feet long and 22 feet deep; then the United States followed with the 704-foot Poe Lock in 1896, the 1,350-foot Davis Lock in 1914, and the Sabin Lock, a twin of the Davis, in 1919. In 1943 the old Weitzel Lock was replaced with the giant MacArthur Lock, 800 feet long, 80 feet wide, 31 feet deep.

The Welland Canal had been overhauled several times. By 1887 its locks were 14 feet deep, 270 feet long—not big enough for the new lake-going vessels. Even if the big boats could have gotten past Lake Erie via the Welland, though, they would have been stopped in the rapids of the St. Lawrence River beyond Lake Ontario.

A Canadian civil engineer, Thomas C. Keefer, offered a clear-cut plan around the turn of the century: build big enough locks and canals to drown the rapids out and make the river navigable all the way to the sea. International commissions were soon being formed, and the United States and Canada began seriously to discuss the creation of an inland waterway such as Keefer proposed.

In 1917 Congressman Bertrand H. Snell of New York introduced a bill authorizing the Secretary of War to consider joining in an international effort to build a seaway "for ocean-going ships . . . in or paralleling the St. Lawrence River." But the bill died in committee. The idea remained alive, though. Seven years later, Secretary of Commerce Herbert Hoover headed a new commission to study the feasibility of building such a seaway.

But, as seems inevitable in any project of this size, there was political opposition. The railroads were unhappy about the competition a seaway would represent, and they fought the plan. Some Americans were uneasy about co-operating with Canada on a project of such scope; suppose our relations with Canada turned unfriendly some time in the future? And there were always those people in faraway parts of the country who resented having their tax money spent on projects of no direct benefit to themselves.

While Congress hesitated, Canada went ahead. It rebuilt the Welland Canal, enlarging it to fit the specifications of the proposed seaway. The new canal, which cost $130,000,000, had a depth of 25 feet, and its 8 locks were 80 feet wide, 859 feet long, 30 feet deep. It was and still is an engineering marvel, a wonderful staircase that easily lifts huge vessels from Ontario's level to Erie's or lets them down the 326-foot grade from Erie to Ontario.

The splendid new Welland Canal allowed the big lakers to travel east as far as Lake Ontario, now. But there they had to stop. Beyond lay the St. Lawrence, with its 22 locks only 14 feet in depth, and its tricky rapids.

The Welland Canal served as an inspiration, though. The year it was finished, 1932, the United States and Canada signed a Seaway Treaty. Treaties have to be approved by a two-thirds vote of the Senate, however. Opponents of the Seaway project kept the treaty from coming to a vote for 2 years.

—and when it did come up, it failed to get the needed majority. The project collapsed, since Canada could not then handle the job alone.

In 1941 President Roosevelt tried to get the plan going again, but the coming of war ended the idea for the time being. And when President Truman revived it after the war, Congress would not approve. The Seaway project seemed doomed to be one of those engineers' dreams, like the tunnel under the English Channel, that everyone talks about but no one builds.

Matters changed rapidly in 1948 when top-grade iron ore was discovered in Canada along the Quebec-Labrador border. The iron ranges of Michigan were playing out, and the industrial cities of the Midwest—Gary, Cleveland, Erie, Chicago, Milwaukee—were hungry for the new Canadian supply of ore.

But getting it from the mine to the Midwest was the problem. A 400-mile rail journey would bring the ore to the St. Lawrence—but then, how could it be shipped up the St. Lawrence, through those 22 shallow locks and those dreadful little antiquated canals? Ore boats are big. A St. Lawrence Seaway was the obvious answer.

In 1934 Canada had needed this country's help. But now, more than a decade and a half later, Canada was far stronger, wealthier. "All right," Canada said to us, in effect. "If you won't help us build the Seaway, we'll build it ourselves!" And in 1951 the Canadian Parliament approved the construction of an all-Canadian Seaway.

This posed a brand-new threat to the U.S. economy. We could not afford to be left out of so important a scheme. Quickly, a compromise plan was worked out that Congress could finally accept. Although neither the Sault Ste. Marie nor the Welland Canals had charged tolls, the new Seaway would. This took care of the objection that taxpayers in the South and West would be footing the bill for a Seaway that would chiefly benefit the Great Lakes area. The Seaway would be self-supporting through tolls, and would pay off its construction cost within 50 years.

The new plan went through Congress in 1954 and was signed by President Eisenhower. Canada gladly accepted our belated offer of co-operation. The plans for the Seaway, which had been on the shelf for 20 years, could be dusted off. The Seaway would be built—not only to provide a new outlet for commerce, but to yield power, power from giant dams.

BUILDING THE SEAWAY

It was a big job, a job to equal the construction of the Panama Canal or the taming of the Tennessee. It took 4 years, cost more than a billion dollars, and at its peak kept 22,000 workmen busy.

The navigation part of the two-pronged task involved replacing the 22 small, obsolete locks on the St. Lawrence with seven new, big ones. Two of these were built by the United States, five by Canada, at an over-all cost of $470,000,000—perhaps the most expensive stairway in the world.

These locks, and their accompanying dams, buried the troublesome rapids forever. But the force of the river remained as irresistible as ever, and this force was harnessed to turn turbines and yield power. And so came the Moses-Saunders Power Dam, one of the six biggest hydroelectric plants in the entire continent of North America; its 32 generators turn out 1,880,000 kilowatts of electricity, divided equally between two power-distributing authorities, Ontario Hydro and the Power Authority of New York.

Four-fifths of the world's ships can use the new route. General cargo ships of 9,000 tons capacity, ore and grain carriers of up to 25,000 tons capacity, can travel the length of the St. Lawrence and the Great Lakes, at tolls cheaper than those on the Panama Canal or the Suez Canal. The new waterway handles ships of 5 to 10 times the capacity of those that could use the old canal system. And electricity from the new power dam lights homes and runs factories from southern and eastern Ontario to the Mohawk Valley of New York, and across Lake Champlain into Vermont.

Construction jobs of this sort are never easy. But building

the St. Lawrence Seaway was tough even by usual standards.

One of the biggest headaches was a kind of clay that the workmen called, expressively enough, "blue goop." This slick, greasy stuff was almost half water, and sloshed around to misery-producing effect when workers tried to handle it. Millions of tons of "blue goop" had to be stripped out of the Wiley-Dondero Canal—named for the Senator and the Congressman who wrote the final Seaway bill—that connects two of the biggest locks, Eisenhower Lock and Snell Lock. The Wiley-Dondero job involved a cut that was 442 feet wide at the bottom and 50 feet deep. But the mucky ooze of the river-bed did not want to sit still. It would slide and slosh around at will, driving the workers to distraction.

Gigantic excavating machines were brought into play. The biggest of them was a 650-ton behemoth that the men nick-named "The Gentleman," which took 25-ton gobbles of "blue goop" and dug out 2,000,000 tons of muck in 6 months. Getting "The Gentleman" to the job was a problem in itself. He was being used to dig for coal in Kentucky when the call went out for his services. His 2,000-mile journey across four of the five Great Lakes took him 102 days, and at one point a bridge had to be lifted from its piers to let the barge carrying him pass beneath.

While the workers at Wiley-Dondero slogged through clay-like ooze, the men building the Beauharnois Locks farther up the river in Quebec Province were having a completely opposite problem. They were up against 3,000,000 tons of Potsdam sandstone, rock so hard that 10 feet of it could blunt a drill bit, so tough that a power shovel was rendered toothless in just 18 hours of work.

The rock had to be blasted, but in order to blast you first have to drill holes in which to plant the dynamite. A conventional compressed-air drill needed a week to sink each of the 100-foot blasting holes at Beauharnois. Construction time-tables couldn't allow that. Instead, the contractors tried shooting jets of flame into the rock at five times the speed of sound. The 4,000-degree jets knifed through the stubborn rock as though it were butter, cutting in at a rate of 10 feet an hour instead of 20 feet a day.

Ooze at one point, implacable hardness at another—and winter everywhere. Today the Seaway has to close down from November to March every year because the river freezes over, but construction work had to go on, right through the winter, even when the mercury quivered at 30 and 40 below zero. The ground was frozen solid. If a workman touched metal with an ungloved hand, his hand would stick, frozen to the metal surface. Lubricating fluid in tractors and excavating machinery froze also. When a digger could be made to work, its load of earth and gravel would often freeze to the steel of the scoop, or to the beds of the trucks into which the scoopers were dumping.

To cope with this, the truck beds were sprayed with oil to insulate the metal from the load. When that did not work, small excavators had to be used to get the dirt *out* of the trucks after the big diggers had dumped it *in!*

Pouring concrete at zero degrees Fahrenheit presented difficulties too, since the concrete had a way of freezing before it was set. The contractors kept the retaining forms warm by spraying them with steam jets. When it could be managed, the concrete-pouring was carried out under canvas tents and tarpaulins. "Salamanders"—fire pots made of punctured oil drums—kept the work area warm.

There was the headache of river ice. When Long Sault Spillway Dam, just upriver from Eisenhower Lock, was half finished in early 1957, an ice jam formed. To finish the job, a new cofferdam had to be put in place, but the ice prevented this. At any moment a flood might crash through the already completed section.

The ice was 30 feet deep, loose pack ice under 2½ feet of hard crystal ice. To break up the jam, Frank Matejka, project manager for the U.S. power engineers, made use of the gates of the incomplete dam. He closed two of them, backing up a third of the river flow, and opened them again quickly. Doing this several times in swift succession created currents that set the ice jam rocking against the sluice walls. The ice began to break up, and in 3 hours was gone.

More trouble harried the dam-building team 3 months later, on June 29, 1957. This time it was a hurricane named Audrey who turned some engineers prematurely gray. Long Sault Dam, which is the half-mile-long control dam that regulates the flow of water to the turbines of nearby Moses-Saunders Power Dam, was just about complete, and was holding water at the 203½-foot-level when word came of flooding upstream. A drop in barometric pressure had "tipped" Lake Ontario; the eastern part of the lake had risen a foot, and 60-mile-an-hour winds were whipping the floodwaters into the St. Lawrence. To make matters nastier, the hurricane knocked out the automatic water-level gauges, so no one along the river knew exactly how much of a flood to expect.

Frantically the men at Long Sault Dam started opening gates to draw down the reservoir in anticipation of the floodwaters. There were 12 gates to lift, only 2 cranes to do the job, and it took 20 minutes to lift each gate. They just barely made it. After lifting gates half the night, they drew down enough water to handle the new rush from the west—but they came within an inch and a half of flood levels!

To widen and deepen the river sometimes involved eliminating bends and angles. Engineers threw up cofferdams and worked behind them, carving a new channel for the river wherever the old one was too angular. Other cofferdams left stretches of the riverbed temporarily exposed. The sharp fangs of Long Sault Rapids baked in unaccustomed sunlight for 9 months, until they were drowned by 38,000-acre Lake St. Lawrence when Moses-Saunders and Long Sault Dams were finished.

The business of pumping parts of the river dry for construction caused snarls on shore. While digging the Seaway channel opposite Montreal, a dike a quarter of a mile from shore was temporarily erected. The result: the wells of the householders on the shoreward side of the dike ran dry! The St. Lawrence Seaway Authority of Canada placated the unhappy residents by buying them water tanks and supplying them with water by truck while the construction continued.

The hardest single part of the operation was building the hydroelectric plant in the International Rapids section of the project. At the Long Sault Rapids, near Iroquois Point, the water level fell more than 90 feet in a short span. A sharp drop like that is always valuable for power generation.

Three structures were needed: a control dam, at Iroquois Point on the Canadian side; a powerhouse, linking Barnhart Island in midriver with the Canadian shore at Cornwall, Ontario; and a spillway, to the west and south of the powerhouse, to control the depth of the power pool and the flow of the river beyond the power project.

One problem was that the power pool would have to flood 18,000 acres of land on the American side and even more on the Canadian. Nor was this uninhabited canyon land, as in the Far West. On the American side there were some 200 farms, 600 homes. On the Canadian side, disruption was even greater: 7 villages, where 6,500 people lived, lay in the path of the projected lake.

The people of the seven villages were saddened at the idea of having to move, but they bowed to progress. The Hydro-Electric Power Commission of Ontario (usually called simply Ontario Hydro) had the job of relocating them. "If you want to keep on living in your old house, we'll move it for you at our expense. If you prefer, we'll build you a new one instead," Ontario Hydro told the townspeople.

The seven towns were moved. Some people grumbled, others welcomed the coming of the Seaway. Some hung out signs on their houses: "WE HAVE TO GO, BUT WATCH US GROW!"

All along the 30 miles of the north shore of what was to be Lake St. Lawrence, the moving went on. Five hundred twenty-five homes were moved, many new ones were built. Graveyards and barns were moved too. A party of archeologists combed the area in search of Indian relics, racing against time to make their final discoveries before the water hid the sites forever, just as is now being done in Egypt around the Aswan High Dam.

While the towns were on the move to higher land, the work gangs were moving in to start constructing the dam, the powerhouse, and the spillway. The river had to be shoved aside to let the men work—and that meant diverting a flow of 236,000 cubic feet of water per second.

Barnhart Island split the river into two channels. The north channel, 2½ miles across, was blocked by two huge cofferdams. One of them, 75 feet high and almost a mile long, was the biggest cofferdam ever built. Between the two cofferdams, pumps worked overtime to dry out the riverbed. A third cofferdam, near the site of the future spillway, completed the task of shunting the river flow entirely through the south channel.

Now Long Sault Rapids stood dry and stark for 30 miles. Construction could begin. The first concrete for Iroquois Dam was poured in November 1955. This dam, at the head of the International Rapids, was intended to control the flow of water coming downriver from Lake Ontario. A gravity-type concrete dam supported by buttresses, Iroquois Dam has 32 gates whose vertical lifts are operated by 35-ton traveling gantry cranes.

The Long Sault Spillway Dam supplies the other half of the pincers between which Lake St. Lawrence is held. The Long Sault Dam barricades the lake at its downstream end, and its 30 gates, 50 feet wide, are used to pen up the reservoir of water from which the power plant draws.

The powerhouse itself is a long, low structure spanning 3,300 feet from Barnhart Island to the north shore of the river near Cornwall, Ontario. Although it is one building, it has two names. The part of it on the American side of the invisible borderline running down the river is called the Robert Moses Power Dam, in honor of the chairman of the Power Authority of New York. The Canadian half of the powerhouse bears the name Robert H. Saunders-St. Lawrence Generating Station, honoring an important Canadian figure. The dam is generally known simply as the Moses-Saunders Power Dam.

The power dam has 32 turbines, through which the penned waters of the St. Lawrence are allowed to flow after they leave the Long Sault Dam Spillway. Its generators, with their output of 1,880,000 kilowatts, are second only to those at Grand Coulee Dam.

This three-part power project, Iroquois Dam, Long Sault Spillway Dam, and Moses-Saunders Power Dam, cost $650,-000,000 to build—$180,000,000 more than went into the navigation part of the Seaway scheme. The three dams were finished early in 1958, and the power pool itself was created in a dramatic ceremony shortly afterward.

It took place on July 1, 1958, on the important Canadian holiday known as Dominion Day. A single cofferdam held back the surging St. Lawrence. Thirty tons of dynamite were embedded in this cofferdam. Crowds gathered on both shores, and after an official dedication ceremony, the dynamite was detonated.

Gigantic chunks were ripped out of the 600-foot cofferdam, at precisely 8 A.M. The river leaped high, pouring through the gaps and washing out the rest of the dam. Swiftly it rolled on, taking an hour to reach the wall of the power-plant dam. Lake St. Lawrence began to back up, covering the old rapids, spreading over the old shoreline, hiding forever the sites of the towns that had been moved.

It took three days for the pool to fill. On the Fourth of July, the first vessel passed through the new locks that had been built: the U.S. Coastguard Cutter *Maple*, which made the passage eastward. Shortly afterward, the Canadian commercial vessel, the S.S. *Humberdoc*, was the first to make the westbound trip through the locks. The first week 263 ships, representing 10 nations, used the locks.

As for the power, it began to flow on July 5. Sixteen American turbines and 16 Canadian ones began spinning, funneling power to both shores. Half the U.S. share of the power is used in the nearby town of Massena. As in the Columbia River Basin, the aluminum industry has come to take advantage of the abundant electricity. The Aluminum Company of America had operated a smelter in Massena since 1903, but now it was joined by an $88,000,000 plant built by Reynolds Metals Company. But the towering high-voltage lines carry the Seaway's power beyond Massena as well, out to the Mohawk Valley and even to western Vermont. Once again, a river had been harnessed to work for man.

AND NAVIGATION, TOO

Power plants are only half of the St. Lawrence Seaway story, of course. The prime reason for building the Seaway was to provide the water route from the Great Lakes to the Atlantic, with hydroelectric power an incidental, though important, byproduct.

Making the river navigable involved three separate assignments: dredging the river to deepen it; widening its channel where that had to be done; and building locks to help ships over the steep drops.

To get a good understanding of the way the Seaway works, let us follow a westward-bound freighter on its trip to the Great Lakes. An ore carrier, let's say, bound for the steel mills of Indiana. Or, better yet, a Dutch ship out of Rotterdam, laden with bicycles for Chicago, heavy machinery for Milwaukee, European goods of all sorts bound for the cities of the Middle West.

As a seagoing ship, the freighter has to be careful its draft is not too great for the 27-foot-deep channels of the Seaway. Lakes and rivers are less buoyant than the ocean. Ships settle deeper in fresh water than in salt, some 3 per cent deeper.

But our ship has a 22-foot draft. No problem at all, so far as the Seaway is concerned.

She enters the St. Lawrence from the broad Atlantic, and the first thousand miles of her journey offer no difficulties, for here the St. Lawrence is wide and deep and open to seagoing vessels of all sizes. Up the river she goes, past the Gaspé Peninsula, the city of Quebec, past Trois Rivières, and Sorel.

But then she reaches Montreal, perched majestically on the hillside, and here the Seaway begins.

For at Montreal the river rises 22 feet. This once was an impassable barrier for big ships, the end of their journey. Smaller vessels could have used the old Lachine Canal with its five small locks to get over the rapids, but larger ones would have had to unload.

Now there is no need to unload. Our ship passes under the handsome Jacques Cartier Bridge and then approaches the easternmost of the Seaway's locks, the St. Lambert, by Victoria Bridge. Into the lock she goes. The gate shuts behind her. Up ahead, water is boiling into the lock through the sluice gate, and the lock, 900 feet long and 80 feet wide, is filling rapidly.

As it fills, the ship rises, slowly, gently. She climbs 22 feet, and a second lock is waiting, the Côte Ste. Catherine Lock, identical in size, to give us another 30-foot boost, and the rapids are past.

Now we leave the river entirely, and pass through a canal that cuts to the south of the St. Lawrence, bypassing troublesome rapids. Then it is on into peaceful Lake St. Louis, formed by a natural widening of the river. At the upstream end, we leave the river again via the Beauharnois Locks, which boost us 82 feet more.

The two Beauharnois Locks take us past the Beauharnois Powerhouse, which generates power out of that 82-foot drop at Soulanges Rapids. Here, too, five old locks used to lift ships before the coming of the Seaway.

Beyond the Beauharnois section, we steam along without difficulty, first along the 30 miles of the 27-foot-deep Beauharnois Power Canal, then into tranquil Lake St. Francis, another of those natural bulges in the river. For the entire distance so far, we have been in Canadian waters. As we pass through Lake St. Francis, the Province of Ontario is on the northern shore of the lake, the Province of Quebec on the southern shore.

But now we are approaching the international section of the Seaway. From the head of Lake St. Francis onward, it is New York State to our left, along the southern shore.

And now the International Rapids Section is coming into view. We pass under the International Bridge, a suspension bridge whose 120-foot clearance is more than sufficient to give us clearance. The International Bridge was erected to replace an older bridge too low to admit the big ships that now would be using the waterway. Beyond the bridge, which is jointly owned and administered by Canada and the United States, we enter the South Channel of the river and head for the fifth of the Seaway's big locks.

This is the Snell Lock, named in honor of that New York Congressman who, in 1917, had introduced the first of many bills asking for the development of the St. Lawrence Seaway. The Snell Lock is not very different from the first four. It is big—860 feet long, 80 feet wide, 30 feet deep. Its massive gate, whose structure reminds one of a waffle with its many indentations, holds back 9,000 tons of water without quivering. Since a lock is a kind of dam, it is not surprising that the gates make use of one feature of dam construction: they arch against the current for greater strength.

We glide into Snell Lock, which marks the beginning of the Wiley-Dondero Ship Channel. Up to the north, in the other channel of the river, is the Moses-Saunders Power Dam, which we are bypassing. The lock gate closes behind us, and water starts to hiss in up front. The lock fills, and we are lifted 45 feet more. Then it is onward for another 3½ miles through the Wiley-Dondero Channel until we reach the next lock, number six, named for President Eisenhower.

Eisenhower Lock is the twin of Snell Lock in all respects but one. There is a highway tunnel running under the Eisenhower Lock, carrying traffic from the New York shore to Barnhart Island in midriver. The downriver Beauharnois Lock also has a four-lane highway running through a tunnel beneath it.

Eisenhower Lock boosts us 44 feet more, and we have completed the 89-foot climb from the level of Lake St. Francis to that of Lake St. Lawrence, the artificial lake created in 1958 to feed the Moses-Saunders Power Dam. Since Montreal, we have climbed 241 feet in six locks—but the journey is a long way from being over.

We pass by the city of Massena, on the New York side, as we continue into the 30-mile-long Lake St. Lawrence. Now we head across to the Canadian side, and get ready for the last of the seven Seaway locks, Iroquois Lock.

The lift here is not particularly dramatic, only 5 feet, in contrast to the 22-to-45-foot lifts of the earlier locks. The Iroquois Lock takes us out of the old riverbed and cuts through Iroquois Point, bypassing the Iroquois Dam that regulates the upper end of Lake St. Lawrence.

We have now been through the 189 miles of the new waterway, and have risen from sea level to the 246-foot height of Lake Ontario. Leaving Iroquois Lock, we now enter the most picturesque part of the St. Lawrence, the Thousand Islands region, a favorite resort area for many years. Here, a great many little islands—not merely a thousand, but actually more than 1,700—dot the St. Lawrence. Some are uninhabited specks of rock that are adorned by nothing more than one or two pathetic, lonely looking trees. Others are giants, 50 square miles in area.

No work needed to be done in the Thousand Islands section except to deepen the channel in places. The water is smooth, the channel broad, and there are no rapids or sharp drops. We continue along the St. Lawrence for the 68 miles of the Thousand Islands section, and then we are at the source of the river—Lake Ontario.

More climbing lies ahead of us. We cross Lake Ontario, heading southward and westward, toward the Niagara Peninsula, that jutting slab of land that separates Lake Ontario from Lake Erie. The mouth of the Niagara River is near us, but we do not enter, for we have no wish to try scaling the 186-foot jump of Niagara Falls. Instead, we take the Welland Canal, older than the Seaway but every bit as impressive in the size of its locks.

In one way, the locks of the Welland Canal are even more impressive than those of the Seaway. The Seaway's locks are single ones; when ships are going through in a westbound direction, the eastbound ships must wait their turn on the side. But three of the Welland's seven lift locks are "twin-flight" locks—an upstream and a downstream lock side by side, so that ships going in opposite directions can pass each other.

Thus there are some surprising vistas to behold in the Welland Canal. We benefit from one now. As we approach from the north, heading up the giant staircase, a ship is coming toward us from the south, traveling downward from high Lake Erie. From the first of the Welland's three twin-flight locks, we can look south, and see the other ship high above us, riding majestically in her full lock as we sit in our empty one.

But then our lock begins to fill, hers to empty. We are treated to the astonishing sight of a giant vessel appearing to sink under the waters of the canal. But those waters are sinking too. And in our lock we are rising.

Our lock is full, now. We have been lifted to the height of the middle lock, and as the gate in front of us opens, we steam forward toward it. The northbound ship is moving, too, upstream into the middle lock on *its* side. For a while, we sit side by side, the other ship in its lock, ours in the southbound lock. But we are at the same level only a short while. Water is swirling out of their lock, for their north gate is open. And our *south* gate is open, letting the water flow in from the higher elevations in front of us.

We rise, they drop. We wave a cheerful goodby, and move out of the middle locks into the locks just ahead. Now we are far above them, and we can look back and see our northbound friends going down, down, down the giant staircase while we continue to rise. And then we move on, and they are lost to sight.

The Welland Canal's seven lift locks span a distance of only 8.7 miles, from Lake Ontario to the town of Thorold. The average lift of each lock is 46½ feet. Nowhere else in the world are big ships lifted so far in such a short distance as at the Welland Canal.

The present Welland Canal, as was pointed out earlier, is the fourth since the first linkage between the lakes in the 1830's. Its huge locks—800 feet long and 80 feet wide—were built, in 1932, to the same scale as those that would be constructed for the Seaway a quarter of a century later. It was not necessary to alter them in any way to make them fit for the new traffic that the Seaway brought. The only work that was done on the Welland Canal when it became a unit of the St. Lawrence Seaway was to deepen the sections between the locks.

The eighth lock on the Welland Canal does not lift. It is a control lock, near the Lake Erie end of the canal, used to keep rein on the waters of the canal during times of high water on the lake. We pass through this final lock, actually a dam of the kind we have been meeting in earlier chapters, and emerge on Lake Erie. We have climbed 326 feet more, in a matter of hours.

Now the Great Lakes are in our grasp. We can stop at Erie, or Cleveland, or Toledo. Or we can continue on, turning northward at the west end of Lake Erie to drop our cargo at Detroit. If our destination is further on, we can continue, from Lake Erie into Lake Huron and along the upthrust "mitt" of Michigan.

Two more lakes lie ahead of us. We can pass easily from Lake Huron into Lake Michigan at the Straits of Mackinac, where the passage is smooth and level, thanks to more man-made artifice. Underwater compensating dikes at Detroit, and an ingenious river-diversion scheme at Chicago, help to keep Huron and Michigan at the same level and guarantee the ease of navigation through the waterway. If we enter Lake Michigan, we can travel to Gary, to Chicago, Milwaukee, Green Bay.

But instead, perhaps, our destination lies along Lake Superior—in Duluth, perhaps, or Port Arthur on the Canadian side.

To make the passage from Lake Huron to Lake Superior, we have to use the Sault Ste. Marie Canal—the "Soo," as it is called locally.

At the Soo locks, the Army Engineers coolly control the level of Lake Superior without pausing to feel astonishment at what they are doing. Since 1922, the largest fresh-water lake in the world has obeyed man's behest. The height of Lake Superior is important to shipping men at the Lake ports; they load their big ore and grain boats to the last permissible inch, and a foot less water would mean that much less cargo that could be loaded. So a compensating dam keeps Lake Superior closely regulated, maintaining a consistent level. A joint commission of the United States and Canada decided that the level of Lake Superior should be kept between 602.1 and 603.6 feet above sea level in the public interest. And so it is. When the rivers that feed Lake Superior are slack and feeble, the dam's gates are shut to keep the water level high. When spring thaws fatten Lake Superior, the gates are opened, sending the excess water sluicing toward Lake Huron and maintaining the proper level in Superior.

Now that we have reached Lake Superior, we have come to the end of our journey on the St. Lawrence Seaway. All up the river, we have seen the effects of the Seaway's coming. The river and the lakes swarm with boats, big boats. The patient toil of thousands of men—the carpenters in yellow hats, the concrete workers in green hats, the steel workers in blue ones—has transformed the St. Lawrence. It was not a job of river "taming"—as has been done on the Tennessee or the Colorado—so much as a job of river *adjusting*. The St. Lawrence was almost good enough to serve man's needs. Now it is better than good enough.

Not that the job is done for all time. *No* power or navigation job is ever finished forever and ever. The population of the United States keeps growing, and so do our industries.

Needs expand with blinding rapidity. Charles Harvey's 350-foot lock at Sault Ste. Marie was considered an oversized folly in 1855, but it was deemed much too small 20 years later.

Bigger ships are being built all the time. Commerce keeps growing in all directions. And the St. Lawrence Seaway will have to grow with it.

One of the first steps will probably be the twinning of all seven of the Welland Canal's locks, to provide two-way travel right through the canal. New locks on the St. Lawrence itself will almost certainly follow, possibly as early as 1970.

Another big leap forward will come when the Seaway can be operated all year round. Keeping a northern river like the St. Lawrence free of ice in the winter sounds like a tall order, but engineers are well on their way to taking care of it. Experiments carried out in Sweden have shown that a channel can be kept ice-free by using air bubbles. Compressors at the bottom of the channel force air up through perforated polyethylene pipe. The action of the air bubbles brings warmer water up from the river bottom, melting the surface ice.

Such blower systems are already at work in two places in Canada. At Prescott, Ontario, the bubbling process keeps a small ferry channel open. And at Huntsville, Ontario, the underwater bubbles have kept a 200-foot channel clear of ice even in subzero weather while a bridge is being built. Beyond doubt the St. Lawrence Seaway will be in year-round operation not many years hence.

New power dams will be needed, too. Time and again it has been seen that generating capacity never can keep up with the demand. In 1935 it seemed that the Grand Coulee Dam would turn out far more power than anyone in the whole Northwest could ever use—but today dozens of power dams are being built on the Columbia River to supplement Grand Coulee's output.

So, too, on the St. Lawrence. As industry grows, new dams will have to rise. The first will most likely be built at the Lachine Rapids near Montreal. Others will follow wherever conditions are favorable for power generation—and, where no favorable conditions can be found, men will *make* them favorable.

In earlier chapters we saw how dams brought power to homes and factories, and irrigation water to thirsty fields. In this chapter, another application of the dam principle has occupied the center of the stage. Man-made walls to hold back water can be used to lift ships of mammoth proportions, as well as to impound reservoirs. The "temporary reservoirs" formed by navigation locks have turned Chicago and Detroit and Duluth into seaports, via the new St. Lawrence Seaway.

9

Problems

~~~~~~

DAMS are useful things. Anyone who remembers the old days in the Tennessee Valley can tell you that. Anybody who lives within a thousand miles of Grand Coulee Dam know how valuable dams are. The farmers of California's Imperial Valley loudly sing the praises of Hoover Dam. The prosperity and welfare of millions of Americans depend directly on the towering, handsome dams with which the nation's rivers have been harnessed.

But dams can cause headaches, too. Dams have drawbacks and disadvantages. In the eyes of some people, these drawbacks and disadvantages are overpowering enough to make them want to condemn the entire dam-building concept.

Let us look at a few of the negative features of dams, and see what is being done to overcome them.

THE FISH PROBLEM

One of nature's strangest phenomena is the way salmon come home to spawn. Every year, in the late summer and early fall, millions of sea-dwelling salmon leave the Pacific Ocean and flock to the mouth of the Columbia River. Fighting against the current, they swim furiously upstream in shining hordes, heading for the places where they were spawned.

Two, four, even six years may have gone by since these salmon hatched, high in the mountain streams. Yet, mysteriously, they return to the place of their birth with an unerring instinct that defies understanding. When they reach the place where they were spawned, the females lay their eggs, and the males fertilize them. Then the old salmon, exhausted by their fierce journey, drift weakly back downstream and die. The newly hatched salmon, called fingerlings, return to the Pacific, only to play the same role in the cycle a few years later.

Salmon swim hundreds of miles upstream to return to their birthplaces. They will leap up rapids, hurtling headlong in seeming defiance of gravity. This return of the salmon is no mere fisherman's legend. In 1948 an experiment at the University of Washington School of Fisheries proved that.

Fertilized eggs of the silver salmon were placed in tanks at the University, in Seattle. After 18 months, the fingerlings that hatched were released, specially marked for later identification. They were placed in the Lake Washington Ship Canal. From there, they made their way into Lake Union, then out into Puget Sound and the sea.

Three years later, 75 adult silver salmon, bearing the identifying marks, returned to the tanks at the fisheries building, to lay their eggs. The cycle was complete.

Fish that must return to their spawning grounds are called *anadromous*. Pacific salmon are not the only anadromous fish, of course. On the east coast, the shad and the Atlantic salmon also swim upstream to spawn, though they do not die after spawning. The steelhead trout lives in the Pacific much of the time, but returns to the rivers at irregular intervals. These are all commercially valuable fish. Important industries are dependent on them.

Anadromous fish can leap barriers with ease—provided these

are low barriers. But what salmon could possibly hurtle the 550-foot wall of Grand Coulee Dam? Even the much lower crest of Bonneville Dam is an impassable barrier for the salmon whose homing instinct drives them upstream.

In the first years of the dam-building boom, no one worried much about the anadromous fish. Their spawning habits were not fully understood. "They'll spawn somewhere else if they can't get past the dam," was the general attitude.

But they did not spawn somewhere else. When a dam rose to block a spawning ground, anadromous fish by the ten thousand would churn at the base of the dam, striving hopelessly to leap the man-made barrier. They leaped until they died of exhaustion.

The owners of the salmon fisheries saw ruin just ahead. If the salmon could not spawn, they would die out—and the salmon-canning industry would die with them! Some way had to be found to get the salmon over the dam and upstream to their ancestral spawning grounds.

The "fish ladder" was the result. Just as river-going vessels can bypass a dam by using a navigation lock, so a series of "locks" enable the fish to get over the dam. A separate channel is created, consisting of a series of little dams that form a row of pools, rising up over the big dam to reservoir level. The salmon, entering the lowest "rung" of the ladder at the base of the dam, could leap from pool to pool until they had crested the dam. Then they could continue on through the reservoir to the spawning grounds. The fingerlings, later, could return to the sea the same way, down the ladder. And in those anadromous species where the adults did not die after spawning, the mature fish could also return to the sea via the ladder.

The first fish ladders worked better in theory than in practice. The fish seemed to prefer to mill around in the splashing water under the spillway, instead of entering the ladder. This was overcome by careful design that put the fish ladder in the place where it was most likely to attract the fish. But then, once in the channel, the fish seemed bewildered by the pools. The slow-moving water was strange to them, and their homing instincts failed them. They tended to collect in the lower pools without going onward.

Millions of dollars went into fish-ladder research. Improvements in design made fish ladders more attractive to the salmon, more like the rapids they were accustomed to. One of the first really successful fish ladders was included in the Bonneville Dam, 42 miles above Portland, Oregon, on the Columbia. Actually there are *two* fish ladders at Bonneville, one along the Washington State bank of the river, the other on Bradford Island at the Oregon side of the dam. But salmon who disdain both these ladders have a third way of getting over the dam. There is an electrically operated fish lock, which functions the same way a navigation lock does. (In fact the fish lock at Bonneville adjoins a 66-foot-lift navigation lock.) The fish swim in, the lock is filled, and they swim out again at the top.

McNary Dam, on the Columbia, was built much more recently than Bonneville, and its fish ladders, though similar, are improvements on the Bonneville design. They were built at a cost of $28,000,000—some indication of how important the welfare of the anadromous fish is considered. At McNary the fish ladders are twin reinforced concrete channels, 2,200 feet long, consisting of a series of pools 30 feet wide by 20 feet long. Foot-high dams separate each pool in the ascending series. On the Washington side of the river, the ladder is supplemented by a fish lock.

The McNary ladders are busy. In 1957, their first year of operation, 292,696 Chinook salmon and 85,460 sockeye salmon used the ladder, according to an official count. More than 100,000 steelhead trout clambered over the dam the same way that year.

Fish ladders are not always practicable from an engineering standpoint. In such cases other steps have to be taken to protect the fish.

The Idaho Power Company had fish problems when it began to construct dams in the Hell's Canyon region of the

Snake River, a Columbia tributary. This private power company was building a three-dam series. As the first two dams, the Brownlee upstream and the Oxbow downstream, rose toward completion, it became apparent that the fingerlings hatched far upstream were perishing as they plunged over the Brownlee spillway on their way to the sea.

Instead of building a fish ladder to get the fish down the 277-foot height of the dam, the power company chose a more elaborate scheme: trapping the fish in the river upstream of the dam, and transporting them by truck and pipeline to a point 15 miles downstream, below Oxbow.

The fish are trapped in a giant steel and plastic net, 120 feet deep and half a mile long, laid across the Snake River. Thick steel cables hold the net in place, and 50 pontoons, each one 38 feet long and 17 feet wide, keep it afloat. The net's mesh is so fine that not even the tiniest fingerling can slip through.

The net prevents the fish, as they come downstream, from being mangled in the turbines or killed as they plunge over the spillway. It feeds the fish into three cleverly designed skimmer traps that sort the fish out by size, through a series of slots. The smaller fish are guided right into an 8-inch rubber pipeline that carries them to a special tank truck waiting on shore. The bigger fish are lifted by hand into tanks on boats, and thence to the tank trucks. And off the fish go, aboard the trucks, to be released far downstream where no dams block their passage to the sea.

At Oxbow Dam, another trap catches the upstream-bound fish heading for the spawning grounds. This trap is not so elaborate, being only a simple fish ladder with a hopper at its head. The adult fish land in the hopper, are conveyed to tank trucks, and get a "taxi-ride" 15 miles upstream, to be released above Brownlee. It costs more than a million dollars a year to maintain this system of fish traps on the Snake River.

Meanwhile, other experiments are going forward to see if fish can be successfully induced to spawn in waters other than their spawning grounds. In the long run, it may save dam-builders millions of dollars to construct fish hatcheries instead of fish ladders. There are many possible solutions to the problem of the anadromous fish, and research is continuing in several different channels.

THE SILT PROBLEM

Lake Mead is doomed. Today, this vast reservoir back of Hoover Dam is clear and deep and beautiful. But it is gradually filling with silt and sedimentation. Huge as it is, it will be nothing but a muck-filled swamp by the year 2225, and Hoover Dam will no longer be of any use for power generation, unless steps are taken to prevent this sediment from accumulating.

The same is true of many of the other reservoirs behind our spectacular dams. Far upstream, where the biggest of rivers is only a fast-flowing creek, silt tumbles into the water. Grains of soil are carried off by the billion and whisked downstream. The creek grows into a stream, the stream into a brook, the brook into a small tributary river, the small tributary river into a roaring torrent like the Colorado—and every step of the way, more and more silt is carried off and transported downstream.

As the river gets stronger, the sedimentation gets bigger. Not only grains of sand, but pebbles, rocks, boulders join the flow. Twigs, branches, then whole tree trunks are swept along. The sudden cloudbursts of the desert country send down deluges that drive great quantities of debris into the river. And on it goes—until it is stopped dead by the concrete wall of a dam. The river drops its load in the reservoir back of the dam. Silt-free water passes through the turbines or over the spillway, and continues on downstream, while the reservoir silts up.

Lake Mead is so gigantic that it will take a long time to fill with sediment. Other reservoirs are filling faster, and each time a reservoir chokes with debris, hydroelectric generating capacity is lost. The only one of the giant reservoirs that has hardly any sedimentation problem is Roosevelt Lake, back of

Grand Coulee Dam. The mountain rivers that feed the Columbia drop their silt en route in upstream lakes before reaching the reservoir. Roosevelt Lake's water is the purest in any of the big dam reservoirs.

Other dams are less fortunate. Elephant Butte Dam on the Rio Grande, in New Mexico, was built in 1916 for irrigation storage, flood control, and power production. A study in 1940 showed that the reservoir was so badly silted that half a million acre-feet of its water-storage capacity was gone. The Rio Grande continued to dump silt until a natural dam of sediment was formed at the reservoir's upstream end, forming new natural lakes upstream that were of no value for irrigation and posed flood control problems of their own. It was necessary to build large dikes to protect upstream property against these unwanted new reservoirs.

Similar stories emanate from other dams. At some, engineers have had to carve new channels through the river-built deltas of sediment in order to keep the generators turning. In others, it has been necessary to build new dams upstream to hold back some of the sediment. But the reservoirs of those new dams are filling up in turn.

Is the whole dam-building program of the 20th century going to be short-lived, then? Are today's billions being wasted to provide power only for the next few generations? Will the sprawling reservoirs of the 1960's be nothing but useless mudholes a century from now?

The silt problem is undergoing constant study. In the chapter on the Hoover Dam, we saw how a series of downstream dams, Davis, Parker, and Imperial, works as a team to desilt the Colorado in its flow beyond Hoover—with a $1,500,000 desilting works at Imperial Dam keeping the All-American and Gila Valley canals free of sediment.

Building desilting works is one answer, if an expensive one, to the slow strangulation of our reservoirs. At Imperial Dam, remember, the river has already been desilted by three upstream dams. The desilting works is only removing the last accumulation. Desilting the Colorado upstream of Hoover would involve an expenditure of many hundreds of millions of dollars.

One way of getting rid of silt is to wash it right through the sluices of the dam. Many dams in high-sediment rivers are designed with scour sluices. From time to time these sluices are opened and the water rushes through, carrying the sediment that has accumulated in the reservoir. One of the most interesting dams in this respect is the Iril-Emda Dam on the Oued Agrioun River in Algeria. The French engineers who built the dam estimated that under normal conditions their reservoir would lose half its capacity to silt in the next 40 years. To prevent this from happening, they designed scour sluices into the dam. These are opened as often as every 2 weeks, and in the rushing flow of water through the sluices hundreds of thousands of tons of debris and muck are scoured out every year. Hydraulic engineers call this technique "flotation transport."

However, this deals only with the lightweight material that comes all the way down to the dam end of the reservoir. Most of the real sedimentation is too heavy to travel all that distance, and is dropped by the river as it enters the reservoir at the upstream end. To handle this upstream natural dam, the engineers at Iril-Emda built a secondary dam of their own, a small one, across the river near the mouth of the reservoir. This dam builds up a junior-size reservoir, which is periodically released into the main reservoir by opening gates in the secondary dam.

As this water rushes into the main reservoir, a violent wave motion is set up. The debris at the upstream end of the reservoir is jolted loose and carried down to the main dam, where it is disposed of through the scour sluices.

The scour sluice idea is a good one for disposing of sediment, and it is used at the old Aswan Dam and many others throughout the world. But it has one important drawback. When the reservoir is opened for scouring purposes, power output drops. Water that should be used for whirling the turbines is cleaning out the reservoir instead.

So the various desilting techniques now in use turn out to be quite costly, either in terms of power lost or in extra money spent on pumps and desilting scrapers. The best way to get rid of sediment, all engineers agree, is to deal with it *before* it gets into the river.

Silt, after all, was once land. Because the land in the river basin was arid and barren, it was easily eroded. But if this erosion can be halted, not only will the silt problem be checked but also new acres will be added to the world's farmland.

Planting along upland river basins is one good way of dealing with silt at the source. Crops, grass, trees—anything that can send down roots will hold the soil and keep it from rushing away downriver. Of course, not every area can be planted. Arid desert canyons simply cannot be turned into garden plots. But even they can be made relatively erosion-proof by bulldozing steep gulleys flat, and by damming them with brush or earth fill and rock so that in time of rain the runoff of water will not be swift and knifelike.

The battle against erosion is intimately linked to the battle to save our reservoirs. Soil conservation programs are vital parts of the over-all engineering aspects of dam-building. Scour sluices and mechanical desilting scrapers can help, but the real work of dealing with silt lies in the field of soil conservation—of keeping the soil out of the river in the first place.

DISASTER PROBLEMS

Engineers try to build dams to last. Every man who has worked on a dam hopes that that dam will live as long as the Pyramids of Egypt. But sometimes dams give way under the continued insistent pressure of the water penned up behind them.

Luckily, these disasters have been comparatively rare in our century. Dams in ancient times often gave way, with catastrophic results for the people living on the downstream, or dry side. Often these accidents were the result of careless dam maintenance over a period of many generations. The shattering of the Marib Dam in Arabia was almost certainly the consequence of decades of neglect.

Today dams are built more scientifically, and they are not allowed to fall into neglect. Most of them are as sturdy as anything in the world can possibly be. Try as hard as it wants, the Columbia River will never succeed in nudging the 22-million-ton bulk of Grand Coulee Dam so much as half an inch off its foundation. Nor will the surging Colorado ever be able to hurl Hoover Dam aside with one heroic swipe.

At least we are fairly confident of this. But confidence in other dams has been sometimes rudely repaid with tragedy.

No doubt the people of the town of Rivaldelago, tucked away in a valley of northwestern Spain, felt as confident of their dam's strength as the people of Washington feel about Grand Coulee. The Spanish dam was the Vega de Tera Dam, built by the Moncabril Hydroelectric Company. Three miles above the village of Rivaldelago, the dam was 2 years old, 112 feet of concrete slab and masonry buttress.

For all of its 2 years, the dam had held back the waters of the Tera River. A reservoir had been forming, $2\frac{1}{2}$ miles long. But it was not yet full, and so the dam had never had a full-scale test of its capacities.

Heavy rainfall fell in all of Zamora Province during the winter of 1958–59, and the Tera River flowed rapidly and high. The Vega de Tera reservoir was filling up as a result. On the night of January 9, 1959, the reservoir reached capacity. Shortly after midnight, the waters mounted to the crest of the dam.

Seventeen of the dam's 28 masonry buttresses gave way under the strain. Moments later, more than 300 feet of the dam's length crumbled and a massive sledge hammer of water poured through and down the 1,700-foot-slope toward the sleeping town. In one deafening cascade, 230 million cubic feet of water descended.

Rivaldelago was flattened. Telephone poles were snapped like matchsticks. Within moments, 123 villagers drowned. Several hundred luckier ones were able to scramble to high ground before the deluge reached them.

This was a case where a dam had simply not been built strong enough to handle the full weight of its intended reservoirs. Heavy rains wrecked it. Bad engineering must be blamed.

Sometimes, though, an act of God that no engineer can foresee wrecks a dam. Dam-builders try not to work in areas of known earthquake prevalence, for instance, and careful sounding is done to make sure the ground is stable before any dam is put up. Sometimes earthquakes are unexpected, though. In Montana, in the summer of 1959, the Hebgen Dam on the Madison River was buffeted by the earthquake that shook up Yellowstone National Park so badly. The 44-year-old earth-fill dam, 87 feet high, cracked, and water spouted through the leaks. But the dam held fast despite this, until it could be repaired. Another dam under the same circumstances might have given way and released its pent-up torrents on the hapless valley downstream.

That same earthquake actually *built* a dam—7 miles downstream from Hebgen Dam. A 20,000,000 cubic yard landslide tumbled into the Madison River, creating a 100-foot lake. The Army Engineers hurriedly cut a spillway channel across the crest of the slide to let the river through, since otherwise a reservoir would have formed behind a not very stable dam that could easily have been washed out again, with grave consequences.

1959 was a very bad year for dams. Having opened with the disaster in Spain, it closed with a far more tragic one in France. The Malpasset Dam, a 200-foot-high arch dam on the Reyran River, completed in 1954, gave way in December 1959. A solid wall of water swept down on the Riviera resort town of Frejus, bringing death to 421 persons. Engineers investigating the catastrophe determined that the foundation rock had shifted along a thin clay seam in the left abutment, making the dam unstable and vulnerable to any serious stress.

We learn from our mistakes. Several other dams of the same type as Malpasset, then under construction in other parts of Europe, were quickly resurveyed in the light of the Frejus disaster. Perhaps it is small comfort to the relatives of those who died when Malpasset gave way, but at least we have emerged with a clearer understanding of such engineering problems, and there will be no repetitions.

THE BOMB PROBLEM

One of the arguments used by enemies of big dams is that the dams create potential dangers for wartime. For instance, Elmer Peterson, the author of *Big Dam Foolishness*, has this to say:

"In this atomic age . . . every large dam above a populated district is a potential death sentence which may be executed easily and without warning. It is a sitting duck. . . . The tremendous magnifying of explosive power made possible by atomic fission, to replace TNT or other familiar explosives, makes the presence of dams a greater war-time menace than ever. . . . One atomic bomb, even if it were not set off in contact with the dam, could do the job because of the incompressibility of water.

"The death-dealing nature of the explosion as such would be only a part of the menace, for the water, rushing from the broken dam, would be instantly contaminated by radioactivity from which there could be no escape."

Mr. Peterson has a valid point here. Certainly in World War II dam destruction formed an important strategic factor. The British RAF blew up three German dams, causing terrific floods that destroyed much of the industrial area of the Ruhr. The Army Air Force destroyed a dam in Italy in 1944, flooding German troops. And, as mentioned earlier, in 1941 the Russians blew up their own Dneprostroi Dam to keep it from falling to the Nazis.

Today, with atomic bombs used in wartime, it would be a simple matter for an enemy to blow up Grand Coulee, Hoover, Bonneville, and the other great dams all in one strike.

Colossal avalanches of water would burst through the shattered dam walls, wreaking unthinkable havoc downstream.

But the best answer the engineering profession can give to this argument is that it is foolish to deprive ourselves of the benefits of big dams simply because they are hazards in wartime. After all, an atomic bomb dropped right in the middle of New York City would cause plenty of havoc too, yet no one is suggesting that we should stop living in cities and take to the hills en masse.

No, the danger of atomic war threatens every aspect of our lives, not merely the reservoirs of our dams. And so, without denying the very great damage that could be caused by atomic explosions at our dams, we must go on building dams, since we need them—and we must devote our energies to the cause of continued peace, so that the bombs will never be able to fall. To stop building dams because they are hazards in time of war would be to hamper our economy needlessly. It would be something like refusing to ride in automobiles because some people have had auto accidents. We cannot live in fear, burrowing in the ground. Certain risks must be accepted if there is to be progress. If you must get from New York to Chicago, taking a train or a plane is faster than, if not as safe as, walking. If you need hydroelectric power and want to control floods or irrigate farmland, you must build dams, and accept the risk they involve.

By driving carefully, a man stays out of automobile accidents. By working hard for peace, we can hope to avoid the bomb-produced floods that the scaremongers warn us about.

10

Other Dams of Today

~~~~~~
~~~~~~

IN earlier chapters we looked in detail at such celebrated dams as Hoover, Grand Coulee, Roosevelt, and Norris. To get an idea of the diversity of dams of all kinds, let us take a quick survey of some of the other dams of today, and then we can go on to consider some of the dams that are now under construction, or proposed, in various parts of the world.

This is as good a place as any to stop to classify the various types of dams. Most engineers recognize seven general types of dams. Three of them are ancient in origin and four have come into general use only in the last 100 years.

The three older types of dams are: (1) *earth* dams, (2) *rock-fill* dams, and (3) *solid masonry gravity* dams.

Earth dams are made of soil that has been pounded down solidly. They are built in areas where the foundation is not strong enough to bear the weight of a concrete dam, and where earth is more easily used as a building material than stone or rock. Some of the biggest dams of the ancient world were earth dams, and, as we shall see in a moment, some of today's giants are of the same type.

Rock-fill dams are formed of loose rocks and boulders piled in the riverbed. A slab of reinforced concrete is often laid across the upstream face of a rock-fill dam to make it watertight.

Solid masonry gravity dams are familiar to us by this time, since Hoover, Grand Coulee, Norris, and most of the other big power dams we have discussed have been of this type. These big dams are expensive to build, but offer advantages of durability and solidity that earth and rock dams cannot match. Solid masonry dams can be built on any dam site where there is a natural foundation strong enough to bear the great weight of the dam.

These three types of dams were all found in the ancient world. In recent decades, four other dam types have come into some use: (1) *hollow masonry gravity* dams, (2) *timber* dams, (3) *steel* dams, and (4) *arch* dams.

The hollow masonry gravity dams are designed very much along the lines of solid masonry dams, but contain only about 35 per cent to 40 per cent as much concrete. Generally the weight of the water is carried by a deck of reinforced concrete or by arches that share the weight burden. The upstream face is usually inclined at a 45-degree angle, and this greater slant spreads the burden over more of the dam body than in a solid dam, requiring less concrete. Hollow masonry dams are harder to build than solid ones, and are practicable only in regions where skilled labor is available fairly cheaply. Otherwise, the labor costs on such a complex dam more than outweigh the savings that result from lighter structure.

Steel and timber dams are not used for major projects. About 1900 an attempt was made to use steel as the major construction element in three large dams. But when one of the three failed to hold, the idea was generally abandoned. Today steel dams are used only as temporary cofferdams needed for the construction of permanent dams. Steel cofferdams are usually reinforced with timber and rock or earth fill.

The timber dam is met on farms and in small lakes, where no great demands are made on it. Timber dams are short-lived, since in a few years' time rotting sets in. Few timber dams are useful more than 30 or 40 years, and must have regular maintenance during that time. However, they are valuable in agricultural areas where a cattle raiser may need a pool for his livestock to drink from, and other such low-level needs.

Arch dams are the most complex big dams. Instead of relying on sheer force of weight to hold back the water, they make use of horizontal arch action. They curve sharply, offsetting the water stresses in a manner that would take many pages to explain adequately. Exactly because arch dams are so complicated from the engineering standpoint, they are rarely built. They are best suited for sites where the dam must be extremely high and narrow. For instance, the Sautet Dam on the Drac River in France, built in 1934, is 414 feet high at maximum, but only 230 feet long at the top of the crest, and 85 feet long at the bottom of the gorge. It is 56 feet thick at the bottom, 8 feet thick at the top.

When it was built, Sautet was the highest dam of its type in the world. But, as we have seen, such distinctions rarely can be claimed by a dam for very long. The Tignes Dam, also in France, completed in 1953, is an arch-type dam that tops Saugnet by 178 feet, rising to a height of 592 feet. But Tignes had to yield the crown in 1957 to the Mauvoisin Dam, on the Dranse River in Switzerland, which at 780 feet is not only the tallest arch dam in the world but, until the completion of Italy's Vaiont 3 years later, was the tallest dam of any type.

SHASTA DAM

Shasta Dam is one of the nation's giants. Situated on the Sacramento River, it is designed primarily as an irrigation dam to benefit California's Central Valley. Shasta is part of one of the most ambitious irrigation schemes to be constructed in the United States since 1847, when modern irrigation first was practiced in this country. (The pioneers were the Mormons of Utah, who on July 24, 1847, diverted creek water to irrigate a potato patch near what is now Salt Lake City.)

Shasta Dam is a concrete gravity dam soaring a majestic 602 feet, second only to Hoover in height among the completed dams of the United States. It helps to irrigate a fabulously fertile area almost 500 miles long and 120 miles wide, larger than all of England.

Before the dams came, the Central Valley was plagued with those twin Southwestern nemeses, flood and drought. When the water in the river was high, it was *very* high; the rest of the time it was a useless trickle, comparatively speaking. On December 2, 1935 the Bureau of Reclamation began building a dam on the upper Sacramento to remedy this situation.

Six and a half million cubic yards of concrete went into Shasta, with a 10-mile-long conveyor belt moving the concrete to the dam site. Thirty-one miles of railroad track had to be moved out of the way, too. The Southern Pacific Railway had been sending trains through the valley for 65 years. A tunnel was drilled under the site of the dam's foundation, and for 2 years the trains passed through this monstrous hole in the ground while construction was going on. The Bureau of Reclamation built new tracks for the Southern Pacific running east of the future reservoir site. Then, when the new railway route was finished, the dam-builders diverted the entire Sacramento River into the tunnel, so that they could build the dam! After the dam was completed the tunnel was sealed up.

The dam has backed up a reservoir of 4,500,000 acre-feet of water. This water is pumped 200 feet up into a canal and carried far to the south, to be turned into the San Joaquin River 120 miles away. This is done because most of the rain of the region falls in the north, while most of the best farmland is in the south. Via first the Delta-Mendota Canal and then the San Joaquin River, the water of the Sacramento is sent some 440 miles to the other end of the Central Valley.

Not only does this provide water for thirsty fields, but it helps to keep the salt water of the Pacific from ruining the San Joaquin Valley. Farmers there, in urgent need of water, had bored more than 30,000 wells. Some of these wells went down more than 2,000 feet and made contact with salt water that had seeped in from the Pacific. Now it is no longer necessary to use this salty, crop-killing water.

The second river of the valley is the San Joaquin River, which in the past used to carry water out of the south, which needed it, and into the north, which didn't. Now that water from the Sacramento was coming southward along the San Joaquin's bed, something had to be done to divert the old northward flow of the San Joaquin. A second dam was built —the Friant Dam—behind whose 319-foot-high walls a reservoir has backed up covering a large area of the San Joaquin Valley. Some of the water from this reservoir is sent northward over the 36-mile Madera Canal to a dry region, but most is diverted farther southward through the 160 miles of the Friant-Kern Canal to the very south end of the valley, where water has always been in highly short supply.

This two-dam arrangement conveniently brings water to the parched fields of the valley's southern end, while freeing the north from its old flood problem. These two dams alone do not solve the flood-drought bugbears alone, of course. Since their completion—the Friant in 1942, the Shasta in 1945—dozens of other dams have been built or planned for the tributaries of the two big rivers, so that the spring flood headache can be checked at its source. Both the Bureau of Reclamation and the Army Engineers are at work in the Valley—the Army Engineers building flood control and power dams, the Bureau of Reclamation building irrigation-and-power dams.

BARTLETT DAM

Few dams are as unusual in their appearance as Bartlett Dam in Arizona. This dam is of the multiple arch type. It is a hollow concrete dam supported by a series of curving arches sloping down into the river, looking like a row of long barrels holding the dam up. Built in 1939, the Bartlett Dam is the highest of its type in the world at 287 feet. Although it is 800 feet long at the crest, the Bartlett Dam makes use of only 182,000 cubic yards of concrete, emphasizing its extreme lightness of construction. (Grand Coulee Dam contains about 50 times as much concrete.)

The Bartlett Dam is an irrigation and flood control dam and does not generate power. It is on the Verde River, a tributary of the Salt River, and was built by the Bureau of Reclamation.

Another big dam of the multiple arch type is the Pensacola Dam on the Grand River in Oklahoma. This power and flood control dam is only half the height of the Bartlett Dam, but is more than eight times as long—6,500 feet across the crest. It was built in 1940.

EARTH-FILL DAMS

The biggest dams in the world, from point of view of volume and length, are the earth-fill dams. Cheaper to build than concrete dams, and more stable where the foundation is inadequate for concrete dams, earth-fill dams have had something of a renaissance in popularity in the last 20 years.

Such earth-fill dams as the Green Mountain Dam of Colorado, the Anderson Ranch Dam in Idaho, and the Boysen Dam in Wyoming are good examples of the type. We previously encountered the Swift Dam in Washington, which until recently was the highest of its type. Davis Dam on the Colorado is also an earth-fill dam.

An earth dam must be designed with a broad spillway channel, since otherwise water passing over the top of the dam will wear away a cut and let the reservoir contents escape. The slopes of an earth dam must be flat and gentle for maximum safety. The downstream, or dry side of an earth dam, must be protected against raindrop erosion, while the upstream side has to be solid enough to stand the impact of waves in the reservoir during times of storm or other turbulence.

There are two methods of building an earth-fill dam: the "rolled-fill" and "hydraulic-fill" methods. In the former, layer after layer of material is placed into the dam site and each layer in turn is packed down tight with rollers. In the hydraulic-fill method, the material is dumped into the river and is washed into place.

To prevent leakage, earth-fill dams are built in layers of different materials. At the heart of an earth-fill dam is usually fine fill—earth and sand. This zone is flanked with zones of water-resistant rock that prevent seepage to the fine core. On the outer borders of the dam, a third zone of rock is placed. No attempt is made to make this outer zone watertight—the middle zone takes care of the leakage problem—but the outer zone is strong and sturdy, to handle any buffeting the dam may get from its reservoir waters. Where drainage is a problem because of a non-watertight foundation, drainage filters under the dam are constructed to carry off the excess leakage. The spillways adjoining an earth-fill dam are lined with concrete, as we saw in the Tennessee Valley. When there is a powerhouse, it too is made of concrete.

The highest earth-fill dam as of this time is the Trinity Dam in California, part of the Bureau of Reclamation's Central Valley Project. Trinity Dam is 538 feet high, 2,450 feet long, and consists of 33,200,000 cubic yards of fill.

Building Trinity involved some very special problems in transportation. The pit from which the earth fill was being taken—known as the "borrow pit"—was almost 1,500 feet higher in elevation than the dam site. About 9,000,000 cubic yards of impervious material had to be hauled down this slope. Instead of using trucks, a high-speed conveyor belt was set up at a cost of $2,000,000. Day in, day out, the belt hauled up to 25,000 cubic yards of fill a day, for the 2-mile distance down the slope to the dam site.

After the core was installed, four other types of fill were laid over it, with outside faces of rock. Trinity Dam is a power-and-irrigation dam, to the northwest of Shasta Dam in the Sacramento Valley region. It backs up a reservoir on the

Trinity River, and this water is then shunted southward into the Sacramento Valley.

The biggest rolled-earth, earth-fill dam, in terms of mass, is the Oahe Dam on the Missouri River, part of a long series of dams that will ultimately bring this unruly river under control. The Oahe Dam was completed in November 1959, after 11 years of work. Some 91,000,000 cubic yards of fill went into the Oahe's embankment.

The purpose of this dam, which was built by the U.S. Army Engineers, is fourfold—power, irrigation, flood control, and navigation. It will back up a reservoir over a 250-mile stretch of South Dakota, gathering the waters of the Missouri at flood time and releasing them when the drought season is upon the land. The Oahe Dam is 242 feet high and stretches 9,360 feet—better than 1¾ miles.

The world's largest dump truck was used to build the Oahe. The 18-wheeled truck had a capacity of 110 cubic yards, or about 165 tons, and when fully loaded could move as fast as 35 miles an hour. As with every dam, special problems peculiar to its individual site arose as construction proceeded. In 1957 a series of slides resulted when the foundation of the dam failed to stand up as expected. It was necessary to modify the design, relocating the power tunnels, and 7,000,000 cubic yards of shale had to be excavated to flatten the powerhouse slopes.

Then, in 1958, came the struggle to close the final 125-foot gap in the dam. This channel, 900 feet long, was whittled down gradually by dumping shale along the banks. The job began shortly after dawn on Saturday, August 2. Two big electric shovels toiled continuously, their 13-cubic-yard buckets scooping again and again to fill the dump trucks, while bulldozers kept the loading zones tidy. Thirty trucks, ten medium and twenty big ones, shuttled back and forth to the gap in the dam, while half a dozen heavy tractors took care of the job of pushing the fill into the channel.

As a channel narrows, the water flowing through it picks up velocity. The Missouri reached speeds of 10 to 12 feet a second, carrying away the fill as fast as it was laid. All through the night, workmen fought the river, trying to close that final gap. It took 21½ hours to turn the trick; the last of the 67,000 cubic yards of fill was dumped a little before sunrise, and the river was dammed.

Granddaddy of all dams, so far as sheer bulk goes, is the Fort Peck Dam, also on the Missouri River. This whale of a dam, built by the hydraulic-fill method, contains 109,000,000 cubic yards of earth, rises to a height of 250 feet, and stretches a dazzling 21,026 feet—almost *4 miles*—across the Missouri in Montana. The Fort Peck Dam was completed in 1939, at a cost of $130,000,000.

No other dam in the world remotely approaches it in length. The Saskatchewan Dam, under construction in Canada, is the runner-up, a full mile shorter across the crest, but the Bosque Dam in Texas, to be completed in 1965, will be 5 miles long. The volume of the Fort Peck Dam is more than ten times that of Grand Coulee, the most massive of the concrete dams. In fact, Fort Peck Dam's volume is greater than that of Oahe, Grand Coulee, and Hoover Dams combined.

In the construction of Fort Peck Dam, four large dredges were built at the dam site, to dredge fill from the valley bottom. The dredged-up material was pumped into place on the dam via steel pipelines more than 2 feet in diameter. At some stages of the operation, these pipelines were as much as 5 miles in length.

The dam was 95 per cent complete when there was a shift in the foundation in the upstream face of the dam, near the east abutment. Such unexpected shifts are a frequent plague in the building of earth-fill dams. Some 5,000,000 cubic yards of fill were involved in the slide. The entire damaged section had to be removed and rebuilt, delaying completion of the dam by more than a year.

Fort Peck's reservoir is of jumbo size too. It covers 245,000 acres and has a 1,600-mile shoreline. When it was first filled, this reservoir, with its 19,412,000 acre-feet of water, was second only to Lake Mead. It has since been topped, in this country, by the reservoirs at the Oahe Dam in South Dakota, the Garrison Dam in North Dakota, and the soon-to-be-completed Glen Canyon Dam in Arizona. As we will see in the next chapter, three new reservoirs in other countries will soon dwarf even Lake Mead.

LE GAGE DAM

Fort Peck is the world's bulkiest dam, and the Vaiont in Italy is the world's highest dam. But someday there may be a more massive dam than Fort Peck, while Vaiont is just on the verge of losing its title to Switzerland's new Grand Dixence.

One dam that will probably hold on to *its* title for the foreseeable future is Le Gage Dam, in France. Le Gage is the world's *thinnest* dam. It was built to generate power, but the French engineers decided to experiment and see just how thin a dam could be built on the site with adequate safety.

Le Gage is about as thin as anyone is likely to dare to build a major dam. It is of the arch design, 125 feet high and 470 feet long at the crest. At its widest point, the base, Le Gage is a mere 8.5 feet thick. It tapers to a slim 4.25 feet of thickness at the crest. (For comparison, Hoover Dam, 726 feet high, is 660 feet thick at the base and 45 feet thick at the crest.)

DRY DAMS

The dry dam is a specialized kind of dam used exclusively in flood control. Dry dams generate no power, they have no value in irrigation, and much of the year they do not even have a reservoir. Nor do they have mechanically operated sluice gates.

A dry dam is simply a barrier across a river upstream from a flood-troubled city. The dam is so placed that a canyon or valley behind it can serve as a reservoir in time of flood. Instead of sluice gates, a dry dam has fixed openings through which the normal water of the river can flow.

During the spring thaws, or during a time of unusually

heavy rains, more water comes down the river than the dry dam's gate can handle at once. Therefore a reservoir starts to form. Water continues to pass through the dam at the normal rate, and the excess is trapped. Eventually all the impounded water has trickled away through the gate in the dam, and the city downstream has been spared from flood.

The best example of a dry-dam system in operation can be seen near the city of Dayton, Ohio, in the heart of what is called the Miami Conservancy District. (There is a Miami in Ohio as well as in Florida.)

In 1913 the Miami River overflowed and destroyed the town of Dayton, then a growing business center in the region. More than 300 people drowned, and property damage ran into many millions of dollars. The town was so badly hurt by the flood that some observers felt it could never be rebuilt.

But Dayton *was* rebuilt. To protect it against another such disastrous flood, five earth dams were constructed in the up-river land above the city. One of these dams is on the Miami River, two are on tributary rivers, and two are on creeks. The dams range in height from 65 to 120 feet, and all have open gates at their bases.

During most of the year, the rivers and creeks run through the gates in these five dams at an even pace. In spring and summer, the flow increases, and the dry reservoirs back of the dams start to fill. But the flow past Dayton is always the same, thanks to the control feature of these dry dams.

These dams have no other function. In fact, plaques placed on these dams carry this inscription:

"The dams of the Miami Conservancy District are for flood prevention purposes. Their use for power development or for storage would be a menace to the cities below."

Where no dry dams have been built, reservoirs must be drawn down to receive floodwaters. But this means a loss of power capacity as the reservoir level drops. For the most efficient hydroelectric purposes, a reservoir should be kept as close to filled as possible. Dry dams have a second advantage in that they are completely self-regulating. They dispose of the floodwaters at their own unhurried pace, and there is no need to decide when to open the gate. The gate is always open, eliminating the possibility of human or mechanical error.

ROCK-FILL DAMS

Rock-fill dams are less common than either earth dams or concrete dams, but there are a goodly number of them in this country. They are composed of layers of various size rock, sometimes with hard-packed earth at their core, and frequently with a concrete slab covering the upstream face. As in earth-fill dams, rock-fill dams must have separate concrete spillways, since water spilling over the top of a rock-fill dam will ultimately set up erosion channels.

The slope of a rock-fill dam does not need to be as flat as that of an earth-fill dam. Earth-fill dams usually have a slope of 3 to 3½ horizontally to 1 vertically, while rock-fill dams can be much steeper, 1.3 or 1.4 to 1.

The Salt Springs Dam, in California, is a typical rock-fill dam. It rests on a foundation of solid rock, with layers of ever smaller rock sloping upward fairly steeply. The upstream face of the dam is protected by a slab of concrete 1 to 3 feet thick, and the lower part of this slab is covered by additional facing made of timber. Despite careful planning, the concrete slab cracked when it was first laid, and it was necessary to empty out the reservoir and carry out repairs, which were successful.

The Salt Springs Dam is 345 feet high. At the time of its completion, in 1931, it was the highest rock-fill dam in the world. Since 1937, though, that rank has been held by another California dam, the San Gabriel No. 1, which is 381 feet high. Almost 11 million cubic yards of rock fill went into San Gabriel No. 1, giving it more volume than Grand Coulee Dam.

An even bigger rock-fill dam is under construction now by the Army Engineers. This is the Cougar Dam on the McKenzie River in Oregon, which will rise to a maximum height of 445 feet and require 13,200,000 cubic yards of fill. San Gabriel No. 1 is used only for flood control, while Cougar Dam's functions will embrace flood control, power production, and navigation.

KARIBA DAM

Three hundred miles south of Victoria Falls in Africa, the biggest man-made lake in the world is just about reaching its full size as this book is written. Until this time, Hoover Dam's Lake Mead, with its 31,142,000 acre-feet of capacity, was the Number One artificial lake of the world. But this new reservoir—backed up by the Kariba Dam on the Zambezi River—makes poor Lake Mead look like an oversized puddle.

This new reservoir has a capacity of 130,000,000 acre-feet of water—which means it holds as much water as *four* Lake Meads, with Grand Coulee's Lake Roosevelt tossed in for good measure.

The dam that has backed up this overwhelming mass of water was completed late in 1960. As dams go, it is not extraordinarily large. Its maximum height is 420 feet, compared with the 726 of Hoover Dam. Its length along the crest is 1,900 feet, compared with the 4,173 feet of Grand Coulee. Kariba Dam's volume is only 1,400,000 cubic yards, about a third that of Hoover Dam and an eighth that of Grand Coulee Dam.

But the gorge back of Kariba Dam was magnificently designed by nature for the assignment of holding the world's largest reservoir. This narrow gorge leads into a gigantic natural basin, and so the reservoir, which stretches 175 miles upstream from the dam, has exceptionally great storage capacity.

Such natural reservoir sites are not found everywhere. Even more unusual, this site turned out to be ideally situated to serve the needs of the growing copper industry of Rhodesia. The dam straddles the Zambezi where it forms the boundary between Northern and Southern Rhodesia, two of the sections of the Federation of Rhodesia and Nyasaland. Its powerhouse, upstream of the dam and 600 feet underground, will be supplying more than 8,000,000 kilowatt-hours of power a year when it reaches full output.

Work on Kariba Dam got under way in 1956, when the International Bank for Reconstruction and Development, an institution that specializes in financing such projects, approved an $80,000,000 loan to the Federation. Other funds, staked by the copper producers, banks, the Federation itself, and Great Britain, provided the $250,000,000 needed to begin work.

The dam-builders encountered some problems that the builders of Hoover Dam and Grand Coulee did not need to worry about. Some 40,000 African natives had to be evacuated from the reservoir area, and some did not like the notion of being uprooted from their tribal homelands. Five hundred tribesmen in the Gwembe Valley in Northern Rhodesia defied the evacuation order, and troops had to be sent in to quell the uprising. Eight tribesmen were killed in the battle.

Floods on the Zambezi in 1957 and 1958 interfered with construction, but the contractors managed somehow not only to stick to their original schedule but actually to get ahead of this. They managed this considerable feat despite the floods, the jungle heat, and the difficulties of building a giant dam in the heart of Africa. As construction proceeded, African chiefs from all over Rhodesia were flown in to watch the work. How these chiefs, still living in primitive jungle huts, reacted to the sight of the concrete monster throttling the Zambezi, we do not know. But it must have been a startling and a terrifying sight to them. How could they have even begun to comprehend that the Zambezi, that 1,600-mile giant in Africa's heart, was about to be harnessed and put to work in the service of man?

11

Dams of Tomorrow

~~~~~~
~~~~~~

DAM-BUILDING goes on all the time, all over the world. Another big dam is finished every month or so, and new ones are begun.

In this chapter, we will look at some of the dams that were not yet finished at the time this book was written. By the time the book has come from the presses, some of the dams in this chapter will no longer be dams of tomorrow, but will be dams of the here and now. Others are farther from completion, and at least one that will be mentioned may never be built at all.

GLEN CANYON DAM

Some time in 1964 the Glen Canyon Dam on the Colorado River will graduate from the ranks of "dams of tomorrow," after 8 years. Glen Canyon will do for the Upper Basin of the Colorado what Hoover Dam does for the Lower Basin. It is a $325,000,000 segment of the $760,000,000 project authorized by Congress in 1956 to begin the job of taming the Upper Colorado.

Glen Canyon Dam is rising 370 miles upstream of Hoover Dam. Between the two big dams, the Colorado River winds its muddy course through a narrow gorge studded with deadly rapids. The most spectacular part of this course lies midway between the two dam sites: the Grand Canyon of the Colorado, which many people feel is the most breathtaking natural wonder in all the world.

The Glen Canyon Dam, which will not harm the scenic beauties of the Grand Canyon region in any way, will be breathtaking in its own way. It will rise 710 feet, making it second only to Hoover Dam in height, among U.S. dams. Its 28,000,000 acre-foot reservoir, 186 miles long, will also be second only to that of Hoover Dam's Lake Mead, in this country. (Glen Canyon's reservoir will be named Lake Powell, after Major John Wesley Powell, that fearless explorer who zipped down the rapids of the Colorado in 1869 and first opened America's eyes to the resources of the Colorado River region.) The big reservoir will serve as a recreation area in Utah—the dam itself is across the border in Arizona—and will permit irrigation of 132,000 acres of what is now desert land.

Before the dam-builders came, only a handful of white men had ever visited Glen Canyon. The only inhabitants of the region were Navajo Indians, who herded sheep on a reservation nearby. Most of the Indians have been moved to a new reservation in Utah, but a hundred of them have stayed behind to work on the dam. One is a foreman.

The dam-builders had to put up a town of their own in the desert. Page, Arizona, whose population is now 6,000, sprang up almost overnight, complete with ten churches, a country club, a supermarket, a bank, a newspaper, restaurants, and everything else that a town of its size ought to have. When the construction workers move on, Page will remain as a permanent town, inhabited by the Bureau of Reclamation people who will staff the dam. As the reservoir area is developed into an important recreation center, motels will mushroom in Page, and prosperity will come to the town that did not exist a few years ago.

Before Page was built, the dam site was remote, isolated, bleak. The nearest town, Kanab, Utah, was 75 miles away. The closest rail transportation could be had only in Flagstaff, Arizona, 135 miles distant. In order to get from one rim to the other of the canyon, it was necessary to drive 190 miles over sandy desert roads.

Roads were built. Plane service was inaugurated—two flights a day out of Page, one to Phoenix, one to Salt Lake City. A soaring bridge, 1,028 feet long, was flung across the canyon—the highest, and second-longest, steel-arch bridge in the country, 700 feet above the river.

Tunnels 2,800 feet long were bored through the canyon rock to serve as diversion channels for the river. That part of the work was finished in February 1959, but a strike for higher pay stopped construction from July to December of that year.

After the halt, work resumed, with scalers being lowered from the rim of the canyon to blast away loose rock, clearing and smoothing the walls, readying them to receive the crushing weight of the dam. Hundreds of thousands of bolts, some of them 20 feet long, were inserted in the face of the cliff. After nuts were tightened on the ends of the bolts, the bolts expanded, keeping the wall from flaking.

A concrete plant was built on a ledge hewn out of the canyon wall. The largest such plant ever used in dam-building, it is capable of turning out 9,600 cubic yards of concrete a day. While this was going up, a cableway system was being stretched across the canyon—two cableways strong enough to carry 50 tons at a time, a third that can handle loads up to 25 tons.

The concrete started to flow in June 1960. The biggest buckets ever used, holding 12 cubic yards of concrete each, started to carry concrete from the mixing plant, out along the cableways, and down into the canyon. Every 5½ minutes, 48 tons of concrete went into place. To cool the concrete as it settled, a refrigerating plant that could turn out 600 tons of ice an hour was constructed.

The reservoir that will be formed will be Y-shaped, 186

miles of one fork extending up the Colorado, 71 miles up the other along the San Juan River, a tributary of the Colorado. Glen Canyon Dam will generate 900,000 kilowatts of power.

Glen Canyon is the biggest single dam in an imposing series that will bend the Upper Colorado to man's whim. Three smaller dams will go up in the immediate vicinity, on tributaries of the Colorado, while others will rise elsewhere in the Upper Basin, 17 dams in all. The first of these, Flaming Gorge Dam in Utah, is almost completed at this time. Others will not begin to yield power until 1968 or 1970. The billion-dollar program has the over-all name of the Colorado River Storage Project, and it is one of the biggest power projects Uncle Sam has ever tackled.

THE BOSQUE DAM

Down Texas way, the Army Engineers have been working since 1958 on a giant rolled-earth dam that will be the longest in the world when it is finished—the Bosque Dam, on the Bosque River, a tributary of the Brazos River. This dam will have a span of 25,000 feet, almost 5 miles from shore to shore.

Construction of the Bosque Dam began in 1958, following the floods in central Texas that did $20,000,000 worth of damage the year before. The dam is designed to prevent such floods, as well as to provide a dependable water supply for the 100,000 residents of Waco, Texas. During the big Texas drought of the 1950's, Waco's water supply dropped so low that water rationing had to be established. The new reservoir should eliminate such problems in the future.

Completion of the dam was originally pegged for 1964, but construction problems have bobbed up. Excessive water pressure in a bed of shale underneath the embankment caused a 1,000-foot section of the embankment to sink 20 feet and slide 20 feet downstream.

The engineers had to wait until the movement of the shale had subsided. Then, to keep it from slipping again, they had to build two huge berms, or earthen buttresses, one on the downstream side of the embankment and one on the upstream side. The concrete spillway, which was already under construction, had to be redesigned because of the slippage. The redesigning will give the embankment double the safety factor it had before, and the spillway a threefold safety factor.

RAMPART CANYON DAM

The Rampart Canyon Dam, as of now, falls into the class of "maybe" dams. The Army Engineers want to build it, and they are currently studying the site—on the Yukon River in Alaska—with great care. The proposed Rampart Canyon Dam will cost $1,300,000,000, and will develop the largest power capacity of any dam in North America or in the world—4.7 million kilowatts, more than double the output of Grand Coulee Dam. The reservoir that Rampart Canyon Dam would create would be on the grand scale—larger than Lake Erie, the engineers estimate. But first the site must be surveyed, and then Congress must approve the project. It may be 15 years or more before Rampart Canyon Dam is built—or maybe never.

LIBBY DAM

Another one of these "maybe" dams is the $330,000,000 Libby Dam, on the Kootenai River in Montana. This one has been in the discussion stage for some years now.

The problem is an international one. The reservoir of the proposed Libby Dam would back up across the border into Canada. In order to build such a dam, a treaty between the United States and Canada is necessary, specifying the share of the power that each country is to get.

A 60-year treaty, called the Columbia River Treaty, was drawn up in 1960 and was ratified by the United States. It covered a number of international questions about dams and electricity. It provided for storage dams to be built at three sites in the Canadian province of British Columbia—Duncan Lake, High Arrow Lake, and Mica Creek. The agreement declared that British Columbia would control the flow of the Columbia River in such a way that power generators at ten

U.S. dams on the river would be able to operate efficiently even at low-water periods. This would insure a year-round power output much larger than is available today.

In return for building the storage dams, British Columbia would receive half the extra power—1,300,000 kilowatts. The United States would also pay British Columbia $54,000,000 for flood control benefits resulting from the new dams. The United States would be permitted to build its projected Libby Dam, with the reservoir crossing the border.

Up till this time Canada has not ratified the treaty. The Premier of British Columbia differs with the Prime Minister of Canada on the way the Canadian share of the power should be distributed, and a political dispute has arisen. Until it is settled, the treaty cannot be ratified, and the Libby Dam project remains on the shelf, along with several other schemes for increasing the power yield from the Columbia River and its many tributaries.

OROVILLE DAM

Another dam that has been delayed by political bickering is the Oroville Dam in California. In 1947 Earl Warren, then Governor of California, signed the law authorizing construction of this dam. But it was not until October 1961 that another Governor of California, Edmund G. Brown, was able to preside over the groundbreaking ceremonies. Governor Brown pushed a button that touched off a huge detonation, and tons of gravel and rock hurtled down into the Feather River Canyon to mark the belated start of construction. Lawsuits and water-rights arguments had held the dam up for more than a decade.

The Oroville Dam will be the tallest in the United States, its 735 feet topping Hoover Dam by 9 feet. Oroville will also be the tallest earth-fill dam in the world. About 80,000,000 cubic yards of gravel, earth, and rock will go into the 6,800-foot-long dam, at a cost of $425,000,000.

Oroville will be a multi-purpose dam. Its reservoir, with a 167-mile shoreline, will serve a flood control function, taking up the waters of the Feather River to prevent such floods as the one that devastated Yuba City, California, in 1955. Then, too, Oroville Dam will generate power, millions of kilowatts of it, from a powerhouse whose design will be highly unusual: it will be built in a concrete plug that will be embedded in the heart of the earth-fill dam, instead of being placed to one side as in most such dams.

Finally, Oroville Dam will provide water for farms and cities. It is the key project in the monumental $1.7 billion California Water Plan, a state-directed program that makes use of an armada of dams, canals, aqueducts, pipes, and conduits to carry water out of California's flood-menaced north into its ever thirsty south.

In the dedication ceremonies at Oroville, Governor Brown said, "We are going to build a river 500 miles long. We are going to build it to correct an accident of people and geography."

What he meant was that only a third of California's population lives in the northern coastal and mountain regions of the state, which get most of the state's rainfall, while two thirds live in central and southern California, which are sunny but drought-ridden. Oroville Dam, when it is completed in 1968, will lend a mighty hand to the job now performed by Shasta Dam, Friant Dam, and others, in diverting the rivers of the north from their natural outlet, the Pacific Ocean, and shunting some of that water to the agricultural area in the Central Valley and to the big cities of southern California.

GRAND DIXENCE DAM

The tallest dam in the world is now under construction in southwest Switzerland. The Grand Dixence, a concrete gravity dam on the Dixence River, will rise to a height of 940 feet by the time it is finished, in 1966. Snow and avalanches limit construction to 5 months out of the year, and so the dam will have needed more than a decade of work before it is completed. It is being built in three stages. The first stage, 584 feet high—itself taller than most dams in the world—was completed in 1960. Now the second and third stages are to be added to bring the dam to its full height.

Switzerland is well suited for building big dams. Its mountain rivers run through regions of hard rock on which great masses of concrete can be rested without fear of collapse. Grand Dixence rests on the sturdy rock known as schist. Other Swiss dams have foundations of granite or gneiss.

And so a great many high dams have risen in Switzerland. Many of them are arch dams, such as the 780-foot Mauvoisin, highest of its type, the 525-foot Lienne, the 490-foot Zervreila. But at least one big earth-fill dam is under construction, the Goschenenalp Dam. At 440 feet, this will be the highest earth-fill dam in Europe, though the Oroville Dam in California will top it by nearly 300 feet.

BHAKRA DAM

A high dam is rising in India's Punjab Province that, when finished, will surpass Hoover Dam by 14 feet. This is the Bhakra Dam on the Sutlej River, a multiple-purpose dam that will help to irrigate 10 million acres of land, produce electricity, and reduce flood hazards.

Construction began in 1956 with the building of a cofferdam 215 feet high. By November of that year, concrete pouring could begin, and the 390-foot first stage of the dam was finished by 1959. Work on the second stage was interrupted by a flood in the diversion tunnel that drowned ten workers and damaged the powerhouse. The tunnel was plugged, and the dam should be complete by 1962.

THE SNAKE RIVER DAMS

The Snake River is a major tributary of the Columbia, and is regarded as one of the last major untapped power canyons in the West. An ambitious dam-building program has been proposed for the Snake River, but up until now it has been held back by two of the continuing feuds of American dam-building: the debate between public and private power interests, and the rivalry between the Army Engineers and the Bureau of Reclamation.

Under an agreement reached in April 1962, the Bureau of Reclamation has assumed responsibility for the middle reach of the Snake River, between Oregon and Idaho. The Army Engineers had proposed the building of the $198,000,000 High Mountain Sheep Dam, with a capacity of 775,000 kilowatts. The Bureau of Reclamation has now taken over this project, but is not planning to go ahead with it until further study has been carried out on fish and wildlife problems in the area. The same dam is involved in a tug of war between the Washington Public Power Supply System, a group of thirteen Washington State public utility districts, and the Pacific Northwest Power Company, representing four private power companies. No decision is likely until at least 1964, when the study of salmon spawning difficulties on the river will be completed.

Many other dams are planned for the region. The Bureau of Reclamation is urging Congress to appropriate money for the $235,000,000 Knowles Dam on the Flathead River in Montana, and the $146,000,000 Garden Valley Project on the Piaute River in Idaho. The Army Engineers are requesting funds for the $210,000,000 Penny Cliffs Dam on the middle fork of the Clearwater River in Idaho.

The full list of proposed and pending dam projects in the Northwest would require many pages. This is the most active dam-building region of the country at the present time.

HELL'S CANYON

One of the infrequent victories for private power came in 1956, in the Hell's Canyon region of Idaho. An 8-year struggle between public and power interests ended in 1955, when the Federal Power Commission granted the privately owned Idaho Power Company permission to build a 3-dam series on the Snake River at Hell's Canyon. The following year, public power advocates attempted to get Congress to authorize Federal construction of a single large dam at Hell's Canyon, but the bill was defeated in the Senate.

Idaho Power has proceeded with its dams. The first, the Brownlee Dam, was completed in 1958. This is the dam whose unusual fish-netting feature was described in Chapter 8. It was followed by the Oxbow Dam, 15 miles downstream, the following year.

The third of the series is nearing completion now. Those who favor private ownership of dams and power generators point proudly to Hell's Canyon as an example of how investor capital can yield satisfactory results in dam-building without expense to the Government. But the public-power adherents insist that, while a power company might be able to build a 3-dam series, it takes governmental billions to create a major project like the Tennessee Valley Authority. They feel that greater private building of dams would lead to a confused and chaotic situation, and that some sort of Government co-ordination is necessary.

RUSSIAN DAMS

In the Soviet Union, of course, there are no arguments about private power versus public power. Under the Communist system the government is the sole employer; there are no privately owned corporations in Russia.

The Russians, with their tremendous eagerness to become a modern industrial nation, have had to build a great many dams in the last few decades to provide power for their factories. One of the first, and most celebrated, of these Russian dams was the Dneprostroi Dam, on the Dnieper River, which was once the biggest dam in Europe, 2,500 feet long and 200 feet high, forming a lake 10 miles wide. Within a few years after the completion of this dam, an entirely new city, Greater Zaporozhie, with a population of 250,000, had sprung into being nearby.

Since the end of World War II, both Russia and Red China have built a great many dams, some of them of considerable size. However, almost no information has reached the West concerning the Chinese dams, while the Russians have released only limited details of what they have been doing.

One major Russian dam now under construction is the Kuibyshev, on the Volga. This is a power-producing dam of the earth-fill variety, with a concrete powerhouse. It will be 100 feet high, and will have a length along the crest of 19,140 feet, making it one of the three or four longest dams in the world.

Another major dam is the Bukhtarminskaya Dam on the Irtysh River, largest of thirteen hydroelectric projects on that river. The chief claim that this dam has to international notice is that it will back up the third largest reservoir in the world, encompassing 43,000,000 acre-feet. This is some 30 per cent larger than Lake Mead. Only the Kariba Dam, with its 130,000,000 acre-foot reservoir, and the new Aswan Dam, which will have a reservoir of 105,000,000 acre-feet, will surpass it.

A big dam-building program is under way on the Angara River in Siberia, which is considered to be the world's largest single potential hydroelectric power source. Kingpin of the Angara River dams is the Bratsk Dam, which will be completed in 1963 or 1964. This dam will have a generating capacity of 4,500,000 kilowatts of electricity—twice as much as Grand Coulee Dam, the previous champion, can turn out at its peak.

A reporter for *The New York Times* was allowed to visit the site of the Bratsk Dam during the winter of 1961. "We halt operations when the temperature drops to 40 below zero," the deputy chief engineer told him. "If there is a strong wind, we close down at 35 below zero."

Despite these severe conditions, 40,000 workers are busily engaged in completing the Bratsk Dam. For all its imposing capacity, Bratsk will quickly be dethroned as the Number One power producer by yet another Russian dam, the Krasnoyarsk Dam on the Yenisei River, which is to have a capacity of 5,000,000 kilowatts.

One dam has already been completed on the Angara River.

This is the Irkutsk Dam, which has been delivering power at a capacity of 660,000 kilowatts since 1958. One third of the Irkutsk Dam's electrical output is fed over a high voltage line to Bratsk, 350 miles to the north, to provide power for construction of that dam. The rest of Irkutsk's power is taken by the new town of Shelekov, where a giant aluminum factory has been under construction since 1957.

Two other dams are also under way in this part of Siberia, the Krasnoyarsk Dam on the Yenisei, previously mentioned, and the Ust-Ilinsk Dam on the Angara. Construction at these dams goes on winter and summer. The workers are given premium pay, 20 per cent above average, as recompense for having to endure the extreme cold of Siberia. They are allowed to spend 15 minutes out of every hour thawing out in front of stoves and open fires.

THE SAKHALIN DAM

The dams on the Angara are now under construction. But the Russians have some other dam-building plans that are still more in the science-fiction stage than anywhere else.

The Russians have given a good deal of thought to building spectacular dams that would drastically alter the world's climate. Some of these dams will never be built, at least not by the Soviet Union, for simple geographical reasons. One of them is a proposed dam across the Straits of Gibraltar that will control the Mediterranean, creating dry land out of the ocean bed. Even if such a dam were possible to build today —which it is not—the political realities would keep the Soviet engineers away. The same is true of another "pie in the sky" Russian dam from Newfoundland to Labrador, designed to keep cold water from coming down out of the Arctic to freeze northern Canada.

But one dam that the Russians may very well build, 10 or 15 years from now, would transform the climate of much of Siberia and Japan. This is the Sakhalin Dam, which the Russians have been dreaming of since 1951.

Sakhalin is an island off the coast of Siberia, just to the

north of Japan. For many years its possession was in dispute between Russia and Japan, but it was occupied by Russia at the close of World War II and is now part of the U.S.S.R.

To the north, Sakhalin is bathed by the Sea of Okhotsk, one of the coldest bodies of water in the world. To the south, the Kuro Shiwo current brings warmth to the island. The Tartar Strait separates Sakhalin from the Siberian mainland. If the warm waters of the Yellow Sea, borne northward by the Kuro Shiwo current, would enter the Tartar Strait, the climate of the entire Siberian coast would be far warmer. But instead of entering the strait, the warm water turns off and enters the Pacific.

The narrowest section of the Tartar Strait is called the Nevelsky Strait, after Gennadi Ivanovich Nevelsky, who discovered it in the 1850's. The Nevelsky Strait is only about 3 miles wide at its narrowest point. During the long winter, it freezes over, and becomes an ice bridge connecting Sakhalin to the mainland. This was convenient for Sakhalin, since the ice, 3 feet thick, gave the island an overland route to the mainland. But it was awkward for Russian shipping. Vessels leaving the port of Vladivostok, in the southern part of Siberia, sailing northward to the ports along the Sea of Okhotsk, could not pass through the frozen part of the Tartar Strait. Instead, they had to make a gigantic detour to the south, going completely around all of Japan via the Pacific, in order to get through to the Sea of Okhotsk.

If only the warm water of the Yellow Sea could somehow be persuaded to flow into the Tartar Strait, everything would be quite different. The Nevelsky Strait would not freeze solid every winter, and so shipping from Vladivostok would not be compelled to take the big detour. And the warm water from the south would make the harsh Siberian climate milder.

As early as 1931, schemes to divert the current were under discussion in Russia. Most of the plans were farfetched and unworkable. But in 1951 the engineer Nikolai Georgievich Romanov visited Sakhalin and studied the situation at first hand. He went on to propose something quite startling: a dam across the 3-mile width of the Nevelsky Strait!

Romanov's idea made use of the tides to assist ships through his dam. The water in the Nevelsky Strait is not very deep, 6 to 10 feet for most of the distance, with a channel 30 to 35 feet deep in the middle. Here, Romanov proposed, a steel lock-gate, 300 feet wide, would be built, floating on pontoons. At high tide, a current of 3 to 5 yards per second would run through this gate. There are two high tides a day, which meant that every 6 hours, at the turn of each tide, the water of the strait would change direction. With each change of tide, ships could pass through the gate, carried along by the rapid current. At low tide, the gate would be closed.

Before the building of his dam, Romanov argued, warm water from the south would pass into the strait, then would flow back again with the low tide. His dam would trap this water on the northern side of the lock, and the strong current would carry it on along the Siberian coast. Three cubic kilometers of water a day—four times more than the flow of the Volga, the Don, and the Dnieper combined—would pass through the lock.

The result would be a gradual warming of the area from Sakhalin north. "The Sakhalin Dam," Romanov wrote, would be "a valve which empties the Yellow Sea into the Sea of Okhotsk by the power of the sun and the moon." The powerful tides would draw the warm water through the strait; the dam would keep it from falling back again. Romanov believes that his dam would raise the average annual temperature on the shores of Lake Okhotsk by as much as 10 degrees in 30 years.

Japan, too, would benefit by the dam. By bottling up the cold waters of the Sea of Okhotsk, the dam would bring about a general warming of the northernmost Japanese islands. The "snow country" of northern Japan would enjoy a year-round springtime.

Of course, building the Sakhalin Dam is a good deal more difficult than dreaming about it, as always. Practical engineering problems remain to be solved. The bed of the strait may not be able to support the great weight of such a big dam. And the side effects have to be studied with great care. It may be that a warming effect of this kind may cause whole-sale melting of Arctic ice, leading to floods along seacoast areas throughout the Pacific. It is never wise to rush into climate-changing projects without taking a long, slow look around first. And so it may not be until 1980 or even later that the Sakhalin Dam is built. It may even turn out that engineer Romanov's plan, which looks so good on paper, is totally unworkable in reality—and the Sakhalin Dam will have to be relegated to the limbo of "engineers' dreams."

This discussion of the Sakhalin Dam is a good place to bring our story of the dam-building idea to its close. We have seen how, in the scant few thousand years of man's history, the idea has evolved—from simple brush and pebble dams that formed little irrigation ponds for prehistoric man, to dams that provided the power to grind wheat and then to generate electricity.

We have seen the modern high dams in operation, with their multiple benefits of power, flood control, and irrigation. And now, a new age of dams is beckoning on the horizon—mammoth dams which, by diverting ocean currents, may be able to transform the world's climate. The generation to come may see dam-building marvels that will make our accomplishments look picayune indeed.

As we have seen, the word "dam" conceals a multitude of meanings. Dams may be made of earth, of rubble, of masonry, of reinforced concrete. They come in a wide variety of sizes and shapes. Some are great thick slabs of concrete, others are delicate, lacy with buttresses. In some, excess water spills over the top, in others at the sides, through tunnels in cliff walls, down chutes, or even up through spouts in the floor of the reservoir.

The variety of sizes and shapes is matched by a variety of uses. There are small dams whose only purpose is to create a pond on a farm. There are dry dams, which hold back water in times of flood. There are recreational dams, built by civic organizations to transform a creek into a lake for swimming and boating.

Some dams are locks, to carry ships up or down a waterway. Some dams are dikes, to hold water in a reservoir or away from inhabited or cultivated land. Some dams are cofferdams, temporary structures that will be swept to oblivion when their job is done.

We have only begun to touch on the complexity of dam-building. Specialized dams of a multitude of types exist, more than could possibly be described here. Wing dams and swing dams, weirs and wickets, diversion dams, storage dams, desilting dams—the vocabulary of dam-building is an extensive one.

And, of course, there are the multi-purpose dams, the giants like Hoover and Grand Coulee, serving a variety of important uses.

Yet despite this seemingly confusing variety of dams, this multitude of uses and shapes and dimensions, it is easy enough to single out the two characteristics that all dams have in common.

One is that they are all devices for restraining and controlling the natural flow of water. Dikes, locks, levees, and all other kinds of dams fit this definition.

Secondly, all dams, whatever their shape or size, whether they are made from concrete or from earth, whether they generate power or collect water for irrigation, whether they control floods or function as locks, serve the same basic purpose: to help man, to work for him, to aid him in the mighty job of conquering his environment, a job that began many thousands of years ago and is still going on today as he stands on the threshold of the universe.

Index

ALLAN H. CULLEN

was born in New York City and was graduated from New York University with a degree in civil engineering. Before settling in Cambridge, Massachusetts, he worked on engineering projects in Italy and India. At present he is in business on a consultant basis which gives him time to indulge in his chief hobby, writing. Mr. Cullen is married and has two young children. Despite his busy schedule, he finds time to indulge in his two favorite pastimes—cooking and playing the bassoon.